Student Book

GCSE Science Skills Booster

How Science Works, Maths in Science and Quality of Written Communication

MARK LEVESLEY

William Collins' dream of knowledge for all began with the publication of his first book in 1819. A self-educated mill worker, he not only enriched millions of lives, but also founded a flourishing publishing house. Today, staying true to this spirit, Collins books are packed with inspiration, innovation and practical expertise. They place you at the centre of a world of possibility and give you exactly what you need to explore it.

Collins. Freedom to teach

Published by Collins
An imprint of HarperCollinsPublishers
77–85 Fulham Palace Road
Hammersmith
London
W6 8JB

Browse the complete Collins catalogue at:
www.collinseducation.com

© HarperCollinsPublishers Limited 2011

10 9 8 7 6 5 4 3 2 1

ISBN-13 978 0 00 745730 4

Mark Levesley asserts his moral right to be identified as the author of this work.

British Library Cataloguing in Publication Data
A Catalogue record for this publication is available from the British Library

Commissioned and project managed by Letitia Luff
Proofread by Jane Roth
Indexed by Jackie Butterley
Designed by Ken Vail Graphic Design
Illustrations by Ken Vail Graphic Design,
    Phil Burrows and Beehive Illustration (Laszlo Veres)
Picture research by Caroline Green and
    Grace Glendinning
Concept design by Anna Plucinska
Cover design by Julie Martin
Production by Arjen Jansen

Printed and bound by Martins the Printers

Credits
With many thanks to: Lianne Parkin, Sheila Williams and Patricia Priest from the Department of Preventive and Social Medicine, University of Otago, New Zealand for providing the raw data from their study (page 36/P4). Lucy English, Chris Pearce and Ed Walsh for their perceptive reviews of the manuscript.

Acknowledgements
The publishers wish to thank the following for permission to reproduce photographs. Every effort has been made to trace copyright holders and to obtain their permission for the use of copyright materials. The publishers will gladly receive any information enabling them to rectify any error or omission at the first opportunity.

Photo credits
p. 44 Wronkiew/WikiMedia Commons, p. 45 Jeremy Mayes/iStockphoto, p. 46 Four Oaks/Shutterstock, p. 51 Andrew Lambert Photography/Science Photo Library, p. 54 Chris Turner/Shutterstock, p. 55 Diego Barbieri/Shutterstock, p. 56 PHILIPPE GONTIER/EURELIOS/Science Photo Library, p. 57br HSE, p. 57tc HSE, p. 57tl HSE, p. 57tr HSE, p. 57bc HSE, p. 57bl HSE, p. 60 Swapan/Shutterstock, p. 61 Franck Boston/Shutterstock, p. 62l iofoto/Shutterstock, p. 62r AISPIX /Shutterstock, p. 64 Chuck Nacke/Alamy, p. 65 Jenny Matthews/Alamy, p. 67 Carolina K. Smith, M.D./Shutterstock, p. 69t Martin Shields /Alamy, p. 69ct wavebreakmedia ltd/Shutterstock, p. 69cl Toranico/Shutterstock, p. 69cc l i g h t p o e t/Shutterstock, p. 69cb Yuri Arcurs/Shutterstock, p. 69b Africa Studio/Shutterstock, p. 71 AFP/Getty Images, p. 72 Fiona Hanson/Press Association, p. 10r Judy Whitton/Shutterstock, p. 10l Per-Anders Pettersson/Getty Images, p. 11r Mau Horng/Shutterstock, p. 11l STEVE GSCHMEISSNER/Science Photo Library, p. 12t Arnoud Quanjer/Shutterstock, p. 13 Maridav/Shutterstock, p. 15 Barcroft Media via Getty Images , p. 14 PASCAL GOETGHELUCK/Science Photo Library, p. 16 NASA, p. 17 DR M.A. ANSARY/Science Photo Library, p. 19 Photos 12/Alamy, p. 21 Caroline Green, p. 22 Carolina K. Smith, M.D./Shutterstock, p. 23 Julius Lothar Meyer, p. 24 KENCKOphotography/Shutterstock, p. 27 Leag/WikiMedia Commons, p. 28 Iain McGillivray/Shutterstock, p. 26 Manchester Evening News, p. 30 Charles D. Winters/Photo Researchers, Inc./Science Photo Library, p. 32t nolimitpictures/iStockphoto, p. 32c , p. 33 RIA Novosti/Alamy, p. 34l brejetina/Shutterstock, p. 34r ERICH SCHREMPP/Science Photo Library, p. 35r AD Singh, P Bhatnagar, B Bybel/Department of Ophthalmic Oncology, Cole Eye Institute and Department of Molecular and Functional Imaging, Cleveland Clinic Foundation, Cleveland, OH, USA, p. 35l AD Singh, P Bhatnagar, B Bybel/Department of Ophthalmic Oncology, Cole Eye Institute and Department of Molecular and Functional Imaging, Cleveland Clinic Foundation, Cleveland, OH, USA, p. 36 Courtesy of David C. Holzman, p. 37 Gary Louth/Manchester Evening News, p. 38 NASA, ESA, and M. Showalter (SETI institute), p. 39 clearviewstock/Shutterstock, p. 40 Tony Hobbs/Alamy, p. 41 David Hawgood/WikiMedia Commons, p. 43 CERN

Contents

For the student

The reason why science is a compulsory subject for much of your time at school is because it teaches you how to think in ways that will help you throughout your life. Science can be divided into two parts:

* learning about what science has already discovered
* learning about how that science has been discovered (scientific skills)

Sometimes we spend too much time in science learning about stuff that scientists have already discovered and so we forget to develop our own skills of scientific discovery. It is these skills that will help you to understand new technology as it becomes available, to interpret data presented on TV and the internet, and to question claims made by people and advertisers.

This book is designed to help you build your confidence in using scientific skills. There's some maths too and there's also help with using English to clearly express your scientific views and ideas.

The book starts with activities to practice skills in a range of contexts in biology, chemistry and physics. There is then a section where each of the skills needed to answer these questions is explained in more detail. So if you get stuck on a question, just follow its link to the relevant skills section. This will help you develop the skills you need to answer the question. Of course, you can use the book the other way around and look at a particular skill that you know you have trouble with. Then follow the links from that skill to the various questions and practice using your skills in different contexts.

Activities

The activities section presents some interesting and relevant scientific stories for you to look at and use your skills to answer the questions.

Questions test a range of essential skills including How Science Works, Maths Skills and Quality of Written Communication. Easy cross references let you look up explanations of the skills needed to answer questions you are struggling with.

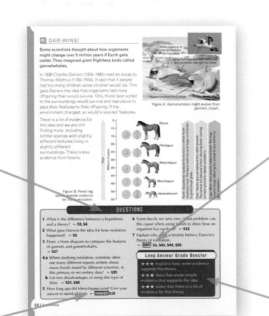

HIGHER The 'Higher' icon flags explanations and questions that will only be tested by students taking the Higher Tier route through a GCSE course.

QWC Where the QWC icon appears next to a question in this book, you will be expected to answer the question using full sentences, good organisation and with correct spelling and punctuation.

Dedicated questions at the end of each activity help you prepare for writing longer answers in exams – there is a booster box to give you hints on how to give a good answer.

Skills

50 core skills taken from the 2011 GCSE specifications are explained in more detail with clear, fully illustrated explanations.

QWC An important part of writing about science is the 'quality of your written communication'. In exams you can lose marks for certain questions if you haven't spelt things right or used the correct format for your answer. Where this icon appears in the skills part of the book, it indicates information about specific QWC skills.

Name Check! is used to identify something that has more than one term to describe it.

Easy cross references let you find questions to practice new skills you want to master

The meanings of all **bold words** in the text can be found in the glossary at the back of the book.

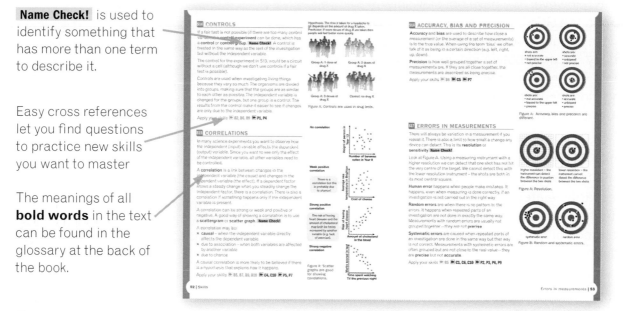

Answers

There are answers to all the questions within the book so that you can easily check your progress. Many of the answers have tips on how you could improve your answers or warnings about mistakes that are often made. So, they're worth reading carefully.

Some answers have an icon, showing you what needs to be done to an answer to make it even better.

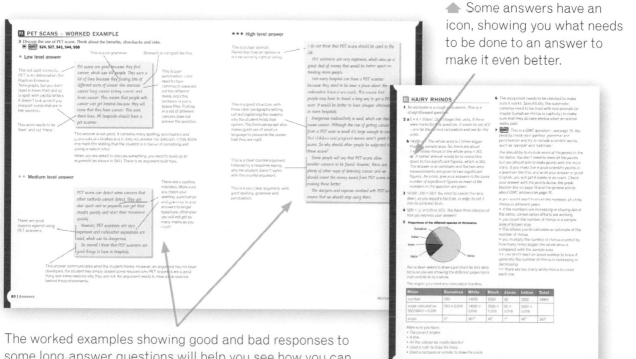

The worked examples showing good and bad responses to some long-answer questions will help you see how you can improve your own answers.

For the teacher

This book is designed to focus on the skills needed for GCSE science, rather than 'content knowledge'. It covers all the skills required by all the different awarding bodies for GCSE in the UK. However, we have not slavishly followed the GCSE requirements. To this end we have included some skills that are not formally required but which are useful in science and may be met by students when doing independent research (e.g. the ability to draw and interpret Venn diagrams).

The first section of the book contains ten scientific contexts for each of biology, chemistry and physics. These contexts are not necessarily related to GCSE specification content. They are simply there to provide a wide range of interesting contexts in which students can apply their skills.

The book is designed to be self-contained and flexible, allowing its use to be dictated by the teacher rather the book imposing a strict, formulaic approach on the way in which skills development is taught.

It is envisaged that most teachers will use the book for intervention. There are a number of ways in which this might be done.

- When students start work on their GCSE courses, it often soon becomes apparent that some students are lacking certain skills. This book allows the students to look specifically at those skills (on pages 44–75). Once covered, they can then practise applying these skills in a wide range of biological, chemical and physical contexts, helping to reinforce the learning and to identify any further areas of weakness/ misunderstanding.

- If you have module tests at half-termly or termly intervals you can analyse student responses from these and then use this book in follow-up lessons to help students improve their skills sets. Again, students would be directed to the skills sections (on pages 44–75) before practising the application of those skills in the different scientific contexts (on pages 10–43).

- An alternative approach is to use the book as a means of assessing mastery of a certain skill or skills. Students would look at one of the scientific context sections and try to answer a selection of or all the questions. An analysis of their answers will then flag up skills that need further attention and the skills sections for those skills can then be looked at.

Each skills section provides links to the biology/chemistry/physics context sections where students can find questions to practise those skills. Since the questions on a skill are not simply written out following the explanation of a skill, this encourages a deeper level of learning about a skill before going on to the questions. It also means that the questions can be properly set in many different contexts.

Questions that allow QWC skills to be practised are flagged up by the various questions in the book.

The chart on pages 7–9 also shows the links between all the different sections, for example following the links from a certain skill will allow you to see which content sections address that skill and to think about which skills to focus on next with students.

However you decide to use the book, we hope that you and your students will find it engaging and stimulating and, above all, give students a major boost in developing their scientific skills and their confidence in using them.

Skills coverage

There are two charts in the book to help you plan your teaching. The simple chart below lists the activities in the biology/chemistry/physics context sections and which skills are practised in them; overleaf the chart continues by listing the skills described in the book, how they are linked and which activities can be used to build them. At the back of the book (pages 113–118) the Skills Statements chart lists statements from the new GCSE specifications and shows how these are covered in the book.

	Activity name	Page	Skills boosted
Biology activities	**B1** Hairy rhinos	10	7, 8, 11, 18, 23, 27, 29, 36, 49, 50
	B2 Salty snacks	11	3, 5, 13, 14, 19, 22, 27, 40, 45, 49, 50
	B3 Dar-wins!	12	1, 3, 4, 10, 12, 25, 37, 43, 49, 50
	B4 Fishy treatments	13	3, 13, 18, 21, 23, 27, 31, 36, 46, 48, 49, 50
	B5 Big brains	14	5, 6, 7, 10, 15, 17, 20, 25, 34, 39, 41, 42, 49, 50
	B6 Plants in space	16	9, 14, 16, 19, 20, 26, 38, 39, 40, 46, 50
	B7 Health scare	17	12, 15, 22, 38, 39, 43, 46, 47, 50
	B8 Clones	18	24, 29, 30, 37, 41, 44, 45, 46, 50
	B9 More than a tan	20	2, 3, 10, 12, 14, 15, 21, 29, 32, 33, 34, 35, 42, 43, 44, 49, 50
	B10 BMI	21	6, 7, 8, 9, 11, 12, 13, 15, 28, 30, 39, 47, 49, 50
Chemistry activities	**C1** Memory of water	22	12, 13, 17, 20, 22, 27, 40, 43, 49, 50
	C2 Periodic table	23	3, 4, 6, 7, 10, 25, 26, 30, 38, 43, 47, 50
	C3 Testing materials	24	6, 8, 9, 13, 18, 19, 21, 27, 34, 38, 39, 40, 42, 44, 47, 50
	C4 Chemistry and war	25	5, 6, 15, 24, 30, 41, 46, 50
	C5 River quality	26	5, 9, 12, 16, 26, 28, 44, 49, 50
	C6 Earth moving	27	2, 3, 4, 6, 9, 17, 37, 43, 49, 50
	C7 Earth warming	28	11, 12, 29, 31, 33, 35, 38, 40, 45, 47, 48, 49, 50
	C8 Airbags	30	6, 8, 13, 19, 23, 24, 26, 27, 35, 44, 46, 49, 50
	C9 Avogadro's big idea	31	1, 6, 9, 18, 27, 30, 34, 35, 40, 43, 50
	C10 Cold packs	32	3, 13, 15, 17, 19, 20, 24, 38, 39, 42, 49, 50
Physics activities	**P1** Cold fusion	33	1, 3, 10, 14, 22, 39, 43, 44, 46, 50
	P2 Galileo's idea	34	1, 5, 6, 7, 9, 17, 22, 30, 34, 50
	P3 PET scans	35	2, 3, 7, 8, 11, 17, 18, 20, 23, 24, 27, 40, 41, 44, 50
	P4 On the socks	36	2, 12, 13, 14, 19, 20, 24, 38, 41, 46, 50
	P5 Sound advice	37	6, 10, 15, 19, 21, 25, 26, 33, 39, 46, 49, 50
	P6 Astronomical	38	3, 4, 17, 27, 35, 38, 43, 49, 50
	P7 SPF	40	13, 15, 16, 20, 24, 27, 38, 42, 45, 48, 49, 50
	P8 Speed limits	41	6, 9, 27, 28, 29, 38, 40, 45, 47, 48, 49, 50
	P9 Measuring distances	42	13, 17, 20, 26, 27, 34, 35, 38, 42, 49, 50
	P10 LHC	43	1, 2, 3, 6, 9, 10, 18, 38, 40, 43, 44, 50

	Skill name	Page	Links to skills	Links to activities		
Developing ideas	**S1** The scientific method	44	S2, S3, S4	B3	C9	P1, P2, P10
	S2 Scientific questions	45	S1, S3, S46	B9	C6	P3, P4, P10
	S3 Hypotheses and predictions	45	S1, S4	B2, B3, B4, B9	C2, C6, C10	P1, P3, P6, P10
	S4 Theories	46	S1, S5	B3	C2, C6	P6
Planning investigations & processing data	**S5** Qualitative and quantitative data	46	S6, S30, S31, 32, S33, S34, S36, S37	B2, B5	C5	P2
	S6 The SI system	47	S7, S8, S10	B5, B10	C2, C3, C4, C6, C8, C9	P2, P5, P8, P10
	S7 Index form	48	S6, S8, S9	B1, B5, B10	C2	P2, P3
	S8 Calculating perimeters, areas and volumes	48	S6, S7, S27	B1, B10	C3, C8	P3
	S9 Compound measures	49	S6, S7, S10	B6, B10	C3, C5, C6, C9	P2, P8, P10
	S10 Standard form	49	S6, S7	B3, B5, B9	C2	P1, P5, P10
	S11 Estimates: rounding and samples	50	S12, S18, S20, S33, S34	B1, B10	C7	P3
	S12 Samples and bias	51	S16, S43	B3, B7, B9, B10	C1, C5, C7	P4
	S13 Variables and fair tests	51	S14, S15	B2, B4, B10	C1, C3, C8, C10	P4, P7, P9
	S14 Controls	52	S12, S13	B2, B6, B9		P1, P4
	S15 Correlations	52	S13, S34	B5, B7, B9, B10	C4, C10	P5, P7
	S16 Accuracy, bias and precision	53	S12, S17, S18, S22	B6	C5	P7
	S17 Errors in measurements	53	S18, S19	B5	C1, C6, C10	P2, P3, P6, P9
	S18 Significant figures	54	S11, S16, S20	B1, B4	C3, C9	P3, P10
	S19 Anomalous results and outliers	54	S20	B2, B6	C3, C8, C10	P4, P5
	S20 Means and ranges	54	S11, S18, S19	B5, B6	C1, C10	P3, P4, P7, P9
	S21 Validity	55	S13, S22	B4, B9	C3	P5
	S22 Repeatability and reproducibility	56	S16, S21	B2, B7	C1	P1, P2
	S23 Trial runs	56	S20, S24, S40	B1, B4	C8	P3, P9
	S24 Safety: risks and hazards	57	S29	B8	C4, C8, C10	P3, P4, P7
	S25 Primary and secondary data	57	S42	B3, B5	C2	P5

Processing data	S26 Symbols and conventions	58	S6, S7, S8, S9, S10, S24	B6	C2, C5, C8	P5, P9
	S27 Fractions, percentages, ratios and decimals	58	S28, S29	B1, B2, B4	C1, C3, C8, C9	P3, P6, P7, P8, P9
	S28 Percentiles, deciles and quartiles	59	S27	B10	C5	P8
	S29 Probability	60	S24, S27, S45	B1, B8, B9	C7	P8
	S30 Tables	60	S13, S38	B8, B10	C2, C4, C9	P2, P7
	S31 Bar charts	61	S5, S13, S38	B4, B6*	C7	P4*
	S32 Histograms	62	S5, S13, S38	B7*, B9	C7*	P8*
	S33 Line graphs	62	S5, S11, S13, S38	B7*, B9	C2*, C7	P5
	S34 Scatter graphs	63	S15, S35, S38	B5, B9	C3, C9, C10*	P2, P6*, P7*, P9
	S35 Gradients and proportion	64	S8, S11	B9	C7, C8, C9	P6, P9
	S36 Pie charts	65	S38	B1, B4	C3*	P10*
	S37 Venn diagrams	65	S38	B3, B8	C6	P9*
	S38 Presenting data	66	S30, S31, S32, S33, S34, S36, S37, S1	B6, B7	C2, C3, C7, C10	P4, P6, P7, P8, P9, P10
Thinking about results	S39 Conclusions	67	S3, S21, S41, S49	B5, B6, B7, B10	C3, C10	P1, P5
	S40 Models	67	S3	B2, B6	C1, C3, C7, C9	P3, P8, P10
	S41 Arguments	68	S39, S48, S49	B5, B8	C4	P3, P4, P7
	S42 Evaluating	68	S16, S19, S21, S22, S39	B5, B9	C3, C10	P7, P9
Science in the world	S43 Exchanging scientific ideas	69	S12, S16, S17, S39, S22, S42, S49	B3, B7, B9	C1, C2, C6, C9	P1, P6, P10
	S44 Benefits, drawbacks and risks	70	S45	B8, B9	C3, C5, C8	P1, P3, P10
	S45 Risks and decisions	70	S11, S24, S27, S29	B2, B8	C7	P7, P8
	S46 Decisions about science	71	S11, S24, S27, S29	B4, B6, B7, B8	C4, C8	P1, P4, P5
	S47 Science in the media	72	S43, S48	B7, B10	C2, C7	P8
	S48 Analysing and synthesising	72	S43, S28, S49	B4	C7	P7, P8
	S49 Note-taking and formal writing	73	S41, S43, S47	B1, B2, B3, B4, B5, B9, B10	C1, C3, C5, C6, C7, C8, C10	P1, P5, P6, P7, P8, P9
	S50 Command words	74	S11, S41, S49	B1, B2, B3, B4, B5, B6, B7, B8, B9, B10	C1, C2, C3, C4, C5, C6, C7, C8, C9, C10	P1, P2, P3, P4, P5, P6, P7, P8, P9, P10

*The skill is practised in this section but not explicitly referred to.

All rhinos have hair but the Sumatran rhino is very hairy.

Due to loss of habitat and poaching, the numbers of all rhinos have decreased. There may only be 250 Sumatran rhinos left, living in a small area. There are about 14 500 white rhinos spread across huge open areas in Africa.

To see if conservation efforts are working, scientists count the rhinos each year. For small numbers of animals in small areas, they try to count each one. Automatic cameras are used to photograph Sumatran rhinos. For white rhinos, scientists use helicopters to count the numbers in one area and estimate the total.

Figure A: Sumatran rhinos live deep in Asian jungles.

Figure B: Helicopters are used to find white rhinos.

QUESTIONS

1 What is an estimate? ▶▶ **S11**

2 a A scientist is estimating the number of white rhinos in a park. She selects a sample area 4 km long and 5 km wide. How big is the sample area? ▶▶ **S7, S8**

  b There are 51 rhinos in the sample. Estimate the number in the whole park, which is a 140 km^2. ▶▶ **S11, S18**

3 What is the ratio of the number of white rhinos to Sumatran rhinos? ▶▶ **S27**

4 Five Sumatran rhinos are found evenly spread over 20 km^2. What is the probability of a rhino being found in any one km^2? ▶▶ **S29**

5 There are also about 60 Javan rhinos left, about 2500 black rhinos and 2650 Indian rhinos. Draw a pie chart to compare the numbers of all five species of rhino. ▶▶ **S36**

6 What needs to be done in a trial run before counting Sumatran rhinos? ▶▶ **S23**

7 How could good data be collected to see if conservation efforts for white rhinos are working? Justify your answer.
  ▶▶ **QWC** **S11, S49, S50**

Long Answer Grade Booster

★★★ justifies answer by explaining why the methods chosen were better than alternative methods

★★★ explains why the data was collected/analysed in this way

★★★ describes how data has been collected/analysed
Remember that this is a **QWC** question – see page 76!

B2 SALTY SNACKS

An advert for a drinks company showed a peanut and said: The Peanut (helping the sale of soft drinks since 1830).

When you eat salty things, like peanuts, your blood becomes a bit more salty. This can cause problems for your body. If your brain detects too much salt in your blood it causes you to become thirsty. The extra water you drink dilutes the salt.

Your cells contain dissolved substances. If cells are put in a solution containing more dissolved substances, water leaves the cells through their cell surface membranes. The cells shrivel up. The membrane only lets water molecules move through it and not the dissolved substances. The movement of water through a membrane that only allows certain molecules to pass through it is osmosis. Figure C shows a model for it.

Figure A: The humble peanut.

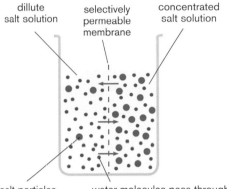

Figure C: Osmosis explained using the particle model of matter.

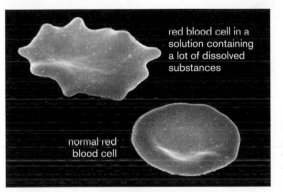

Figure B: Blood cells shrivel in high concentrations of dissolved substances.

QUESTIONS

1 Young children should not eat small items like peanuts because there is a risk of about 1 in 100 000 of them choking to death. Calculate this risk as a percentage. ▶▶ **S27, S45, S50**

2 Is the data in Figure C qualitative or quantitative? Explain your reasoning. ▶▶ **S5**

3 Use the information presented to define a selectively permeable membrane. ▶▶ **S49, S50**

4 Why do scientists use models? ▶▶ **S40**

5 a An investigation is done to see what concentration of salt solution causes a human cell to start to shrivel. Explain why more than one cell is used. ▶▶ **S19, S22, S50**

b What control could be used in this investigation? ▶▶ **S14**

c Suggest two control variables for this investigation. ▶▶ **S13, S50**

6 Some blood cells are put in pure water. Explain what will happen. ▶▶ **QWC** **S3, S49, S50**

Long Answer Grade Booster

★★★ uses a model to explain why the cells swell up

★★★ uses a model to describe how the cells swell up

★★★ states that the cells will change shape

Some scientists thought about how organisms might change over 5 million years if Earth gets colder. They imagined giant flightless birds called gannetwhales.

In 1838 Charles Darwin (1809–1882) read an essay by Thomas Malthus (1766–1834). It said that if people had too many children some children would die. This gave Darwin the idea that organisms had more offspring than would survive. Only those best suited to the surroundings would survive and reproduce to pass their features to their offspring. If the environment changed, so would a species' features.

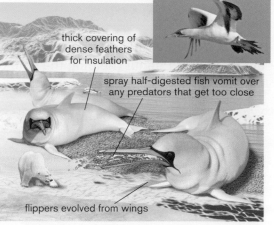

thick covering of dense feathers for insulation

spray half-digested fish vomit over any predators that get too close

flippers evolved from wings

Figure A: Gannetwhales might evolve from gannets (inset).

There is a lot of evidence for this idea and we are still finding more, including similar species with slightly different features living in slightly different surroundings. There is also evidence from fossils.

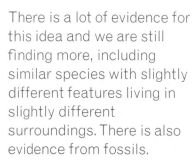

Figure B: Fossil leg bones provide evidence for horse evolution.

Time — Millions of years

Equus

Pliohippus

Merychippus

Mesohippus

Hyracotherium

Teeth: Grasslands replaced the forests in which horse ancestors lived. The back teeth became larger and harder to grind tough grass.

Feet: Harder ground replaced the softer ground. The central toe became a hoof, allowing faster running on hard ground to escape predators.

Legs: More open ground replaced forest. The legs became longer allowing the animal to see further to spot predators.

QUESTIONS

1 What is the difference between a hypothesis and a theory? ▶▶ **S3, S4**

2 What gave Darwin the idea for how evolution happened? ▶▶ **S3**

3 Draw a Venn diagram to compare the features of gannets and gannetwhales. ▶▶ **S37**

4 a When studying evolution, scientists often use many different reports written about many fossils found by different scientists. Is this primary or secondary data? ▶▶ **S25**

b List two disadvantages of using this type of data. ▶▶ **S25, S50**

5 How long ago did Merychippus exist? Give your answer in standard form. ▶▶ **HIGHER S10**

6 Some fossils are very rare. What problem can this cause when using fossils to show how an organism has evolved? ▶▶ **S12**

7 Explain why most scientists believe Darwin's theory of evolution. ▶▶ **QWC S1, S43, S49, S50**

Long Answer Grade Booster

★★★ explains how some evidence supports the theory

★★★ describes some simple evidence that supports the idea

★★★ states that there is a lot of evidence for this theory

B4 FISHY TREATMENTS

People who swim in the Kangal hot spring in Turkey claim that its skin-eating fish, *Garra rufa* and *Cyprinion macrostomus*, can treat skin problems.

Psoriasis (*'sore-eye-a-sis'*) is a condition in which the body sends faulty signals to skin cells, causing patches of dead skin. A pilot study tested the idea that *Garra rufa* can treat psoriasis. 67 patients had a bath with between 250 and 400 fish for 2 hours each day, as well as using a sunbed. The patients were between 10 and 75 years old.

After 3 weeks, the patients were given a 'PASI score' out of 72 (which measures how bad psoriasis is). The mean PASI score at the start was 18.9. At the end it was 5.34. The patients were also asked questions, some of which are shown in the table:

Figure A: Fish such as *Garra rufa* feed on dead skin.

Was there a reduction in ...	Answered: 'Extremely'	Answered: 'Considerably'	Answered: 'A little'	Answered: 'Not at all'
... itching?	46	15	2	0
... pain?	48	6	0	0
... skin scaliness?	60	10	1	0

QUESTIONS

1 What hypothesis was tested in the study? ▶▶ QWC S3

2 Where did the idea for this hypothesis come from? ▶▶ S3

3 List the dependent, independent and control variables in this study. ▶▶ S13, S50

4 How many significant figures are the mean PASI scores given to? ▶▶ S18

5 A 'pilot study' is like a trial run. State two benefits of a trial run. ▶▶ S23, S50

6 a Convert the figures in the table into percentages. ▶▶ S27

b Draw a bar chart and three pie charts to display the percentages. ▶▶ S31, S36

c Which do you think is the better way of displaying these percentages? ▶▶ S31, S36

7 A website advertising a *Garra rufa* treatment claims the study 'shows that people with psoriasis obtain clear benefits from treatment with *Garra rufa*'. Write a short article, explaining what you think about this claim. ▶▶ QWC S21, S46, S48, S49, S50

Long Answer Grade Booster

★★★ explains how the strengths/weaknesses of the study affect the conclusions that can be drawn

★★★ explains why some aspects of the study are strengths/weaknesses

★★★ identifies some strengths/weaknesses of the study

Organisms survive by changing their behaviour to respond to changes in their environments. Our brains are vital for this.

Scientists think that during human evolution, brain size increased to allow more complex behaviour, such as balancing on two legs and language. Evidence comes from measuring the volumes of skulls from human ancestors (Figure A).

Figure A: The scatter graph uses data from the papers of many scientists.

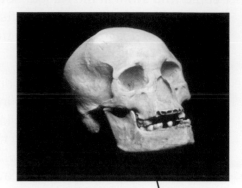

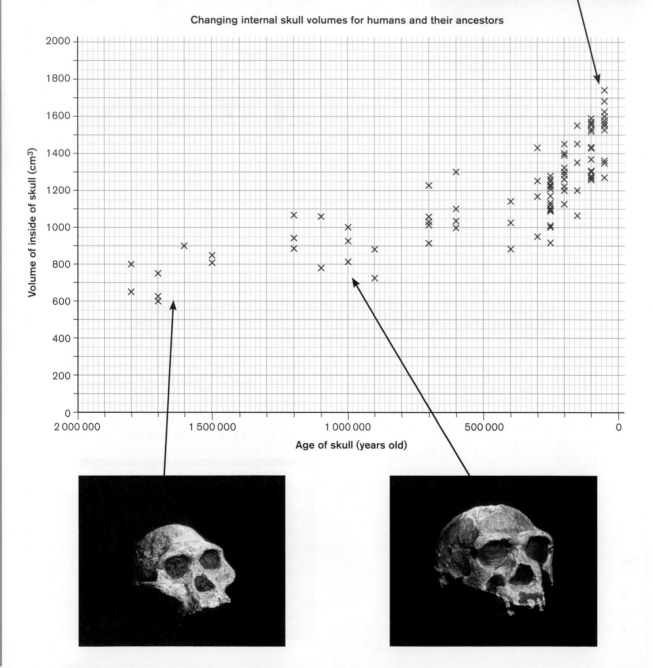

Changing internal skull volumes for humans and their ancestors

Volume of inside of skull (cm³)

Age of skull (years old)

Some scientists say that there was a steady increase in the size of the brain as modern humans evolved, which supports the idea that evolution is a slow continuous process. Other scientists say that there is a sudden increase in brain size about 200 000 years ago, which supports the idea that evolution happens in sudden jumps.

An assumption is something that you think is accepted as correct and so you don't try to show that it is correct. An assumption made by the scientists who produced the graph in Figure A is that the bigger the skull the more brain it will contain. From dissecting dead bodies, scientists have known for a long time that the inside of the skull is mainly taken up by the brain. New techniques (brain scans) have confirmed that this is true and not that the brain suddenly gets bigger when you die. However, brain scans have revealed some people who lead normal lives but whose brains do not fill their skulls. Brain scans like this are anomalous results.

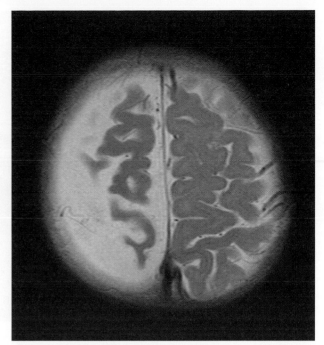

Figure B: Scan from a girl born with only half a brain. She has a normal life.

QUESTIONS

1 a What symbol is used for the unit for volume in Figure A?
  b What does the symbol mean? ▶▶ **S6, S7**

2 What are the volumes of the two oldest skulls? ▶▶ **S34**

3 a What is the range of skull volumes 600 000 years ago? ▶▶ **S20**
  b Calculate their mean. ▶▶ **S20, S50**
  c How would you show the means and ranges for each measurement on a graph? ▶▶ **S34**

4 Is the data in Figure A:
  a qualitative or quantitative?
  b primary or secondary? ▶▶ **S5, S25**

5 Describe the correlation in Figure A.
  ▶▶ **S15, S50**

6 Write '1 800 000' in standard form.
  ▶▶ **HIGHER S10**

7 A scientist argues that increasing brain size allowed human behaviour to become more complex. Figure A is used as evidence.
  a Suggest a counterargument. **QWC**
  b Suggest two assumptions that have been made in using Figure A as evidence.
  ▶▶ **S41, S42, S50**

8 Why is the data used for Figure A likely to contain random errors? ▶▶ **S17**

9 Which idea in the paragraph at the top of this page do you think is more likely to be right? Justify your choice.
  ▶▶ **QWC S34, S39, S49, S50**

Long Answer Grade Booster

★★★ refers to different possible interpretations of the data

★★★ explains choice by interpreting the data

★★★ chooses an idea and some data

NASA scientists have been studying how to grow food plants in the cramped conditions in a spacecraft carrying astronauts to Mars. They have found that LED lights don't produce much heat, so plants can be close to the lights and not wilt.

Figure A: Potato plants at NASA being grown under LED lights.

Substances in a plant take in (absorb) light and use the energy to power photosynthesis, to make food. In photosynthesis, a series of chemical reactions split water into oxygen and hydrogen. The hydrogen is then combined with carbon dioxide to make a sugar called glucose. The oxygen is released.

$$6CO_2 + 6H_2O \rightarrow C_6H_{12}O_6 + 6O_2$$

carbon dioxide + water → glucose + oxygen

Figure B: Word and symbol chemical equations for photosynthesis.

Different LEDs produce different colours and so scientists have investigated which colour is best for photosynthesis. The table shows the results from some pondweed.

Colour of light	Volume of oxygen released in 1 minute (mm^3)			
	Test 1	Test 2	Test 3	Test 4
white	66	69	67	66
blue	60	58	58	55
green	22	17	180	21
yellow	24	22	23	23
red	51	51	50	51

QUESTIONS

1 Explain why models are useful. Illustrate using an example from this page. ▶▶ **S40, S50**

2 What does the formula $C_6H_{12}O_6$ tell you about glucose? ▶▶ **S26**

3 Which figure in the table would you not use to draw conclusions? Explain why. ▶▶ **S19**

4 For which colour are the readings the most precise? ▶▶ **S16**

5 Calculate means for the data. ▶▶ **S20, S50**

6 What compound unit of measurement could be used for the results? ▶▶ **S9**

7 Draw an appropriate graph or chart to display the means. ▶▶ **S38**

8 Why are controls useful? Illustrate using an example from this page. ▶▶ **S14, S50**

9 You have been asked to choose the colour of LED to be used for growing food plants on a spaceship. Outline how you would make this choice. ▶▶ **QWC** **S39, S46, S50**

Long Answer Grade Booster

★★★ explains the full range of evidence needed

★★★ interprets the evidence in the table and list some other evidence needed

★★★ chooses a colour based on the evidence in the table

In the UK, most children are vaccinated against measles.

In 1998 Dr Andrew Wakefield published a peer-reviewed paper in which he tested 12 children to find a link between a vaccination and autism (a communication disorder). Parents of 8 of the children said that their child's autism started just after an MMR vaccination (against measles, mumps and rubella).

Wakefield claimed that MMR was not safe. Some newspapers ran headlines like 'Why I wouldn't give my baby the MMR jab'.

However, one journalist discovered that solicitors working for the parents of the 12 children had paid Wakefield. The solicitors wanted to sue the makers of MMR and needed evidence against the makers.

In some later research, Wakefield needed blood from children. He obtained it by paying 22 children £5 each at his son's birthday party.

Other scientists have not been able to repeat Wakefield's findings. In 2010, he was found to have been 'dishonest' and 'unethical'. He was banned from being a doctor.

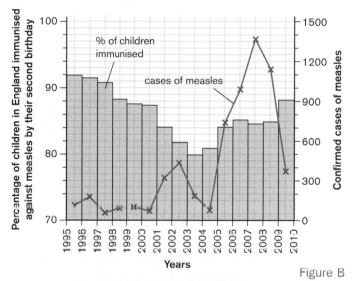

Figure A: Measles can kill.

MMR uptake versus measles cases

Figure B

QUESTIONS

1 What sort of graphs are shown above? ▶▶ **S38**

2 What is a peer-reviewed paper? ▶▶ **S43**

3 a A journalist accused Wakefield of altering his data. Suggest why Wakefield might have biased his data on purpose. ▶▶ **S43, S50**

  b Suggest a cause of accidental bias that might be in Wakefield's data. ▶▶ **S12, S50**

4 a Describe the correlation shown in the graph.

  b Is it is causal? Explain your reasoning. ▶▶ **S15, S50**

5 Suggest one reason why Wakefield should not have made claims about MMR based on his paper. ▶▶ **S39, S50**

6 Explain one way in which Wakefield acted unethically. ▶▶ **S46, S50**

7 How does other scientists' work go against Wakefield's conclusions? ▶▶ **S22**

8 Explain why it is important that newspapers are careful when reporting scientific claims. ▶▶ **QWC S47, S50**

Long Answer Grade Booster

★★★ explains the effects, using an example, of influencing public opinion

★★★ describes, using an example, how a scientific claim can influence public opinion

★★★ states that a scientific claim can influence public opinion

A clone is an exact copy of an organism.

It took 277 attempts to achieve Dolly the cloned sheep in 1996. CC the cloned cat arrived in 2001 after 188 attempts. Today the highest success rates are about 1 in 20.

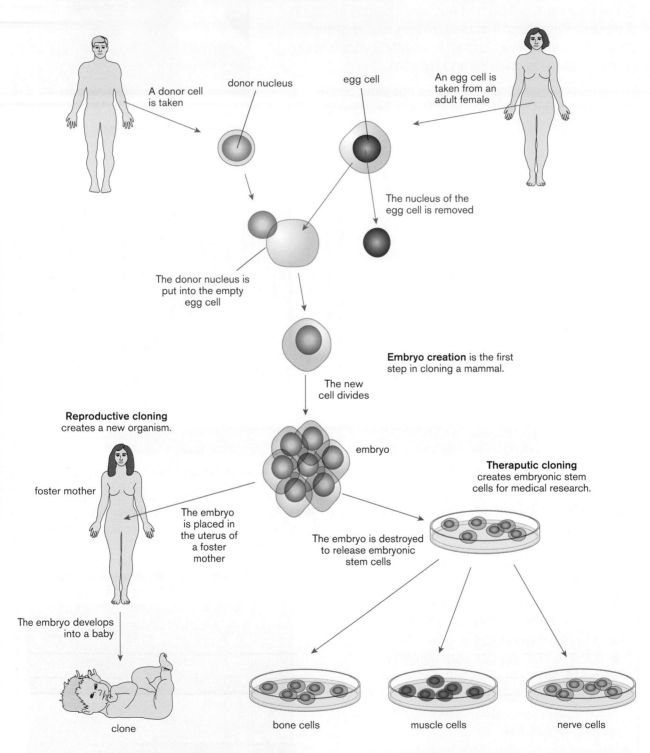

A donor cell is taken

donor nucleus

egg cell

An egg cell is taken from an adult female

The nucleus of the egg cell is removed

The donor nucleus is put into the empty egg cell

Embryo creation is the first step in cloning a mammal.

The new cell divides

Reproductive cloning creates a new organism.

foster mother

embryo

Theraputic cloning creates embryonic stem cells for medical research.

The embryo is placed in the uterus of a foster mother

The embryo is destroyed to release embryonic stem cells

The embryo develops into a baby

clone

bone cells

muscle cells

nerve cells

Figure A: Therapeutic and reproductive cloning.

Cloned animals may not be exactly like their 'parent'. For example, CC is very shy but her 'parent' was the opposite. Some cloned animals have abnormalities or die young (e.g. Dolly died at half her expected age). However, cloning is big business for pets, farm animals, race horses etc. One woman paid £25 000 to clone her dog.

In the UK, scientists can create human embryo clones but must destroy them after 14 days. This allows research into embryonic stem cells, which might be used to mend parts of the body – therapeutic cloning. However, some people want to create cloned babies – reproductive cloning.

Figure B: Could reproductive clones be used to make 'clone armies'?

QUESTIONS

1 Draw a Venn diagram to compare therapeutic and reproductive cloning.
▶▶ S37

2 Display the information about Dolly and CC in the first paragraph as a table. ▶▶ S30

3 Calculate the probability of successfully producing a cloned mammal today.
▶▶ S29, S50

4 The owners of a fast racing greyhound want to clone him. State a benefit and a drawback.
▶▶ S44, S50

5 When donating egg cells for cloning research, about 10% of women become ill. Suggest why a woman might accept this level of risk.
▶▶ S45, S50

6 Rewrite the following sentence using the words 'hazard' and 'risk': Egg cells are obtained using a sterile needle, which helps prevent infection. ▶▶ S24

7 'This research raises ethical and moral issues.' What does this mean? ▶▶ S46

8 Construct an argument for or against human reproductive cloning. Justify your opinion.
▶▶ QWC S41, S50

Long Answer Grade Booster

★★★ uses well structured argument with evidence

★★★ uses reasons in favour and against

★★★ states an opinion with a reason

There are two main types of ultraviolet rays from the Sun that reach the surface of the Earth – UVA and UVB. Too much exposure to ultraviolet rays (especially UVB) can cause skin cancer.

Malignant melanoma is a dangerous skin cancer. There is now a 1 in 91 chance of a British man getting a malignant melanoma in a lifetime, and a 1 in 77 chance for a woman. There are increasing numbers of people getting this cancer. One hypothesis is that people are going on more foreign sunshine holidays. Another hypothesis is that the ozone layer has been getting thinner (ozone absorbs UV rays from the Sun).

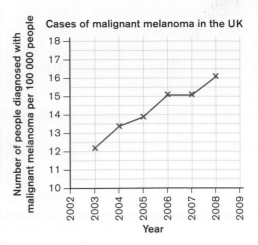

Cases of malignant melanoma in the UK

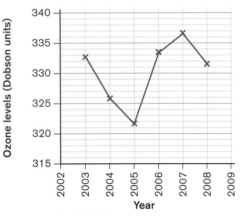

Number of holidays abroad taken by UK residents

Figure A

Changes in ozone levels above Reading, UK

QUESTIONS

1 What scientific question are the two hypotheses addressing? ▶▶ **S2**

2 a Which hypothesis does the evidence in the graphs support? Explain your choice. ▶▶ **QWC** **S3, S15, S50**

 b Suggest a problem with using this evidence to support this hypothesis. ▶▶ **S21, S42, S50**

3 How could you manipulate the data in the graph of ozone levels to make it support the hypothesis that thinning ozone is causing the increase in malignant melanomas? ▶▶ **S12, S33, S43**

4 a Show the number of foreign holidays taken in 2006 in standard form. ▶▶ **HIGHER** **S10**

 b Calculate the rate of increase in the number of foreign holidays between 2003 and 2006. ▶▶ **S35, S50**

5 Make predictions for the cases of malignant melanoma in 2002 and 2009. ▶▶ **S34**

6 Use this page and section P7 (on page 40) to describe the benefits, drawbacks and risks of sunbathing. ▶▶ **S44, S50**

7 What is the percentage probability of a man getting malignant melanoma? ▶▶ **S29**

8 Another hypothesis is that the likelihood of you getting malignant melanoma depends on your use of sunbeds. What evidence would you collect to show this? Explain fully what control you would use for your data and why this is important. ▶▶ **QWC** **S14, S29, S32, S49, S50**

Long Answer Grade Booster

★★★ explains how a control is used when processing the results

★★★ describes the control that will be used

★★★ plans a survey

Each year the National Child Measurement Programme (NCMP) measures the heights and masses of Year 6 children.

18.7% of Year 6 children were obese in 2010. Obese people are likely to have health problems caused by being very overweight. Causes include lack of exercise and eating lots of sugar and fat.

The BMI is an estimate of whether someone has a healthy mass:

$$BMI = \frac{mass\ (kg)}{height^2\ (m^2)}$$

The table shows the different BMI categories for adults. People under 20 are still growing and so their BMIs are compared with those of people of the same age and sex (Figure B).

BMI range	Category
below 18.5	underweight
18.5 – 25	healthy
25 – 30	overweight
above 30	obese

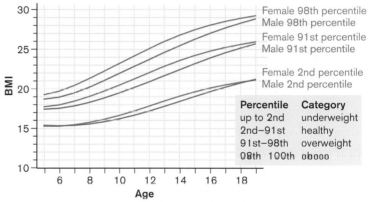

Figure A: This drink contains over a quarter of the total amount of sugar recommended for a whole day.

Figure B: Percentiles used to work out BMI categories for those under 20.

Percentile	Category
up to 2nd	underweight
2nd–91st	healthy
91st–98th	overweight
98th–100th	obese

QUESTIONS

1 Calculate the BMIs of the following and put each person in a category. ▶▶ **S9, S39, S50**
  a Derek is 25, has a mass of 99 kg and is 181 cm tall. ▶▶ **S6, S30**
  b Jane is 12, has a mass of 43 kg and is 1.36 m tall. ▶▶ **HIGHER S28**

2 a What does the symbol 'm²' mean? ▶▶ **S6, S7**
  b State a quantity that's often measured in m². ▶▶ **S8, S50**

3 The BMI is an estimate. What is an estimate? ▶▶ **S11**

4 Suggest one variable that is difficult to control in the NCMP. ▶▶ **S13, S50**

5 10% of children opted out of being measured in 2010. Why is this a problem? ▶▶ **S12**

6 The study found a negative correlation between obesity and wealth. What does this mean? ▶▶ **S15**

7 Suggest why you think the manufacturers of the drink in Figure A advertised it as being 'nutritious' but were then banned from using this word in the adverts. ▶▶ **QWC S47, S49, S50**

Long Answer Grade Booster

★★★ explains why the product is 'nutritious' and/or is not 'nutritious'

★★★ describes some problems with using the word 'nutritious'

★★★ states some reasons why the word 'nutritious' was used

A 1988 paper by Jacques Benveniste (1934–2004) claimed that water 'remembered' chemicals that had been dissolved in it. The editor of Nature, John Maddox, published it on condition that he went to the lab to check the work.

Benveniste took a chemical that causes certain white blood cells to lose granules that they normally contain. He mixed one part of the chemical with 9 parts of water to make a 10 × dilution (1×10^1). He repeated this to make a 100 × dilution (1×10^2) compared with the original. He made dilutions down to 1×10^{120}. The number of cells that lost their granules when added to each dilution was counted.

Benveniste's results always showed a certain pattern of peaks, meaning that some dilutions always had an effect even though they can't have contained any molecules of the chemical. When Maddox visited, the results in the graphs here were obtained. Maddox also discovered that the experiment did not always work but if this happened the results were ignored by Benveniste and his team. This was not stated in the paper.

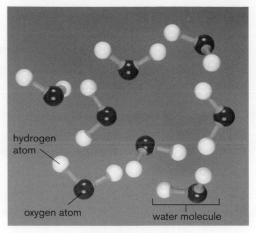

hydrogen atom

oxygen atom

water molecule

Figure A: Are water molecules permanently affected by chemicals?

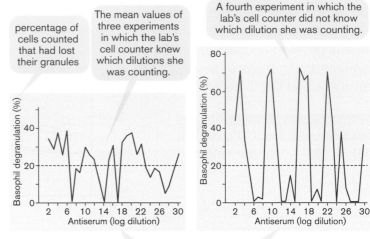

percentage of cells counted that had lost their granules

The mean values of three experiments in which the lab's cell counter knew which dilutions she was counting.

A fourth experiment in which the lab's cell counter did not know which dilution she was counting.

The number on this scale is the index (power) of ten of the dilution – e.g. 1×10^{20} is written as 20.

Figure B: Graphs from experiments during Maddox's visit.

QUESTIONS

1 a Why do we use models? ▸▸ **S40**
  b Suggest one good point and one poor point about the model in Figure A. ▸▸ **S40, S50**

2 What is the ratio of hydrogen to oxygen in a molecule of water? ▸▸ **S27**

3 Explain how a 1×10^4 dilution of the chemical would be made. ▸▸ **S27, S50**

4 a What is the ratio of the ranges in the two graphs in Figure B? ▸▸ **S20, S27**
  b What do the graphs tell you about the results in Benveniste's paper? ▸▸ **S22**

5 Suggest two control variables for this experiment. ▸▸ **S13, S50**

6 Suggest why Maddox published Benveniste's paper. ▸▸ **S43, S50**

7 Benveniste's original results always showed a specific pattern of peaks. Use information from this page to explain how this could have happened. ▸▸ **QWC** **S12, S17, S49, S50**

Long Answer Grade Booster

★★★ explains the effects of the errors

★★★ describes the causes of the errors

★★★ states that this was due to errors

C2 THE PERIODIC TABLE

A Russian chemist, Dmitri Mendeleev, is often called the 'father of the periodic table'. But not in Germany!

Mendeleev wrote a data card for each known element, which he put in order of 'atomic weight' (the *mass* of 6.02×10^{23} atoms). He noticed a pattern and so arranged his cards as a table so that elements with similar properties lined up. He left gaps for elements that he said must exist but hadn't been found. He also swapped some elements around, saying that their 'atomic weight' measurements must be wrong. He published his table in a paper in 1869.

A German scientist, Julius Lothar Meyer, had published a similar table in 1864. It also had a gap but only showed half the known elements. In 1870, he published a complete table, working out groupings of elements from his graph are shown in Figure B.

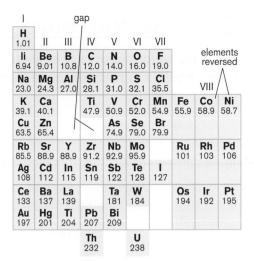

Figure A: An early periodic table by Dmitri Mendeleev (1834 – 1907). There's a modern version on page 126.

Lothar Meyer plotted 'atomic weight' against the volume that that mass of an element occupied. The regular peaks show a pattern of similarities.

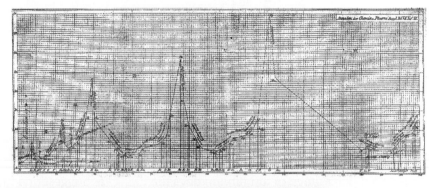

Figure B: The graph published by Julius Lothar Meyer (1830–1895).

QUESTIONS

1 State two predictions made by Mendeleev. ▶▶ **QWC** S3, S50

2 In what way could Lothar Meyer's 1864 idea not be considered a theory? ▶▶ S4

3 a What element now fills the gap next to zinc (Zn) in Mendeleev's table? Use the periodic table on page 126 to help you. ▶▶ S26, S30

b Why was its discovery important for Mendeleev's idea? ▶▶ S4

c How did Lothar Meyer's work support Mendeleev's idea? ▶▶ S4

4 a What sort of graph is that in Figure B? ▶▶ S38

b Suggest units for the two quantities plotted on the graph. ▶▶ S6, S7, S50

5 a Did Mendeleev use primary or secondary data? ▶▶ S25

b Give one disadvantage of this sort of data. ▶▶ S25

6 State one advantage of using symbols for the elements. ▶▶ S26, S50

7 Write out 6.02×10^{23} as a decimal. ▶▶ **HIGHER** S10

8 Papers are usually peer reviewed. Describe what happens and the benefits of this process. ▶▶ **QWC** S43, S47, S50

Long Answer Grade Booster

★★★ explains all the benefits

★★★ describes the steps and describes a benefit

★★★ describes the overall process

C3 TESTING MATERIALS

Alloys are solid mixtures of a metal with other elements. 'Alloy wheels' are pricy because they are made out of expensive metals.

Alloys have a lower density than steel and so are lighter but have the same strength. They are often used for car engines and wheels. Density is mass divided by volume.

The strengths of some alloys of titanium and manganese were investigated. One bar of each alloy was put in a machine that stretched it. The force required to make the bar yield (suddenly get thinner) was measured.

Figure A: This 'alloy' is aluminium with 7.1% Si and 0.4% Mg.

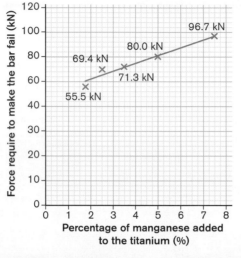

Figure B: Alloys are stronger than a pure metal when stretched.

Graph: Force require to make the bar fail (kN) vs Percentage of manganese added to the titanium (%)
Data points: 55.5 kN, 69.4 kN, 71.3 kN, 80.0 kN, 96.7 kN

QUESTIONS

1 a What percentage of aluminium does the wheel in Figure A contain? ▶▶ **S27**

   b Draw an appropriate chart or graph to compare the percentages of the three elements. ▶▶ **S38**

2 State two ways in which you would make the testing of the alloys fair. ▶▶ **S13**

3 a Estimate the strength of pure titanium. ▶▶ **S34, S50**

   b Which results on the graph would you check? Explain your choice. ▶▶ **S19, S50**

4 State each force on the graph in newtons to two significant figures. ▶▶ **S6, S18**

5 a A steel block of mass 32 g measures 1 cm by 2 cm by 2 cm. Calculate its density. ▶▶ **S8, S9, S50**

   b The same-sized block of aluminium alloy has a density of 2.7 g/cm³. Calculate its mass. ▶▶ **S27, S40, S50**

6 Suggest one benefit and one drawback of alloy wheels. ▶▶ **S44, S50**

7 Three conclusions from the experiment are:

   i – The alloy with 7.5% manganese will be the best of them to use to support a bridge.

   ii – The alloy with 7.5% manganese will be the best of them to use for a crane hook.

   iii – We should use 20% manganese for a crane hook because it will be even stronger.

   Evaluate the conclusions. ▶▶ **QWC** **S21, S39, S42, S49, S50**

Long Answer Grade Booster

★★★ evaluates the investigation

★★★ identifies a mistake in the other conclusions

★★★ chooses a conclusion, with a reason

Fritz Haber was a German chemist who prolonged World War I.

The Germans had been making explosives using naturally occurring sodium nitrate from Chile but in the war their supply was cut off. Haber had invented a process to make a poisonous gas called ammonia, which can also be used to make explosives. Haber's method was improved to make vast amounts of ammonia for the German war effort.

Two reactions happen in the Haber process: hydrogen and nitrogen combining and ammonia splitting. Eventually these two reactions occur at the same rate, with the amount of ammonia forming being equal to the amount of ammonia splitting.

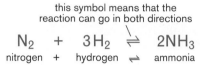

this symbol means that the reaction can go in both directions

$$N_2 + 3H_2 \rightleftharpoons 2NH_3$$

nitrogen + hydrogen ⇌ ammonia

Haber found that using high temperature, high pressure and a catalyst he could get more of the hydrogen and nitrogen to form ammonia. Haber's process is still used today and most ammonia is used to make fertilisers.

Graphs to show the percentage of ammonia produced at different temperatures and pressures

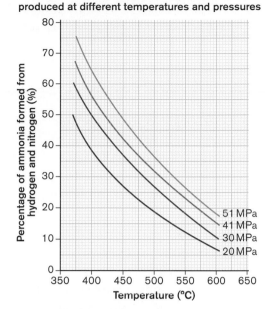

Figure A: High pressures produce more ammonia but increase costs. Lower temperatures produce more ammonia but much more slowly (which increases costs).

QUESTIONS

1 a What unit of pressure is used on the graph?
  b What does this unit mean? ▶ S6

2 a What is the correlation between temperature and ammonia formed?
  b Is this a negative or a positive correlation? ▶ S15

3 Draw a table to show the percentages of ammonia formed by the different pressures at 500 °C. ▶ S30

4 a State one hazard of making ammonia.
  b How might the risks be reduced? ▶ S24

5 a List the variables shown on the line graphs.
  b Describe the variables using these words: independent, dependent, quantitative, qualitative, continuous, categoric. ▶ S5, S50

6 Today, the Haber process is carried out at 450 °C and 20 MPa. Suggest why this set of conditions has been chosen. ▶ S46, S50

7 Construct an argument in favour of building a new ammonia factory in a town. ▶ QWC S41, S46, S50

Long Answer Grade Booster

★★★ uses well structured argument

★★★ explains reasons in favour and against

★★★ states an opinion with a reason

All rivers in England and Wales are graded from A to F.

HIGHER In order to grade each river, various factors are measured, including the concentration of ammonia (NH_3) and the percentage of dissolved oxygen. 36 water samples are collected in 3 years and the measurements are split into percentiles (see table). For example, for grade A the 10th percentile of all the dissolved oxygen readings must be at 80% (or more). The overall grade is the lowest grade given for all the measurements.

Figure A: The River Irk became a bubble bath after a soap factory spill.

Too much ammonia in river water is poisonous to water creatures. Ammonia levels are increased by sewage and by fertilisers. The nutrients in fertilisers also allow algae in the water to grow very quickly. When the algae die, they are broken down by bacteria, which use up the oxygen. This means that there is not enough oxygen for water creatures and so they die.

Grade	A	B	C	D	E	F
Dissolved oxygen (%) at the 10th percentile	80	70	60	50	20	<20
Ammonia (mg/dm³)* at the 90th percentile	0.25	0.6	1.3	2.5	9.0	–

*simplified from original

QUESTIONS

1 Use the information in the table to give one example of qualitative data and one example of quantitative data. ▶ S5

2 What does its symbol tell you about ammonia? ▶ S26

3 What does the symbol < mean? ▶ S26

4 Identify a compound measure used on this page. ▶ S9, S50

5 Suggest why 36 samples of a river are used to calculate a grade. ▶ S12, S50

6 State two drawbacks of using chemical fertilisers. ▶ S44, S50

7 Here are the percentiles for 36 readings for a river.
HIGHER

Percentile	5	10	25	50	75	90	95
Dissolved oxygen (%)	75	79	84	89	92	94	94
Ammonia (mg/dm³)	0.02	0.02	0.03	0.05	0.1	0.18	0.24

a Are these readings precise? Explain your answer. ▶ S16

b State what these figures mean and explain what the river's grade should be. ▶ QWC S28, S49, S50

Long Answer Grade Booster

★★★ clear explanation of percentiles

★★★ grade given using both oxygen and ammonia levels

★★★ grade given with reasons

C6 EARTH MOVING

In 1912 a weather scientist, Alfred Wegener (1880–1930), proposed that the continents were originally joined but gradually moved apart. This 'continental drift' hypothesis explained many observations as shown in Figure A.

Wegener's theory also explained mountain formation; mountains formed when the land rose due to the edges of continents crashing into each other.

Many scientists disagreed with Wegener because he could neither explain how continents moved across a solid sea floor nor show that they were actually moving. In addition, he was not a geologist, he was German (people were suspicious of Germans in the time leading up to World War 1) and other theories had simpler explanations for the observations (e.g. a land bridge had connected South America and Africa).

In the 1950s, scientists discovered that the Earth's crust was cracked into huge plates and these were all slowly moving. This evidence supported Wegener's ideas from 1912. 'Plate tectonics' is a theory based on Wegener's ideas and is what most scientists believe now.

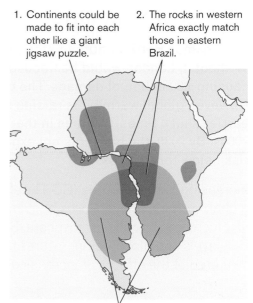

1. Continents could be made to fit into each other like a giant jigsaw puzzle.

2. The rocks in western Africa exactly match those in eastern Brazil.

3. Fossils found in southern Africa exactly match those found in parts of South America.

Figure A: Observations explained by continental drift.

Figure B: These 200 million-year-old fossil sea creatures are over 0.5 km up in the French Alps.

QUESTIONS

1 a Suggest a scientific question that Wegener asked. ▶ **S2, S50**

b What was his hypothesis? **QWC**

c Suggest a prediction that he made. ▶ **QWC S3, S50**

d Explain why 'continental drift' was a 'theory'. ▶ **S4, S50**

e How would Wegener's theory explain the fossils in Figure B? ▶ **S4**

2 Suggest why the moving of continents could not be measured in 1912. ▶ **S17, S50**

3 Suggest a measurement unit for the speed of the Earth's plates. ▶ **S6, S9**

4 Jules Marcou, a well-respected geologist, developed the land bridge theory. Suggest one reason why scientists believed Marcou and not Wegener. ▶ **S43, S50**

5 Arrange the observations on this page into a Venn diagram to show which observations are explained by 'plate tectonics' and which by 'land bridges'. ▶ **S37**

6 Write a short article about how the theory of 'plate tectonics' developed. ▶ **QWC S49, S50**

Long Answer Grade Booster

★★★ explains differences between theories

★★★ well-structured article

★★★ states the theories, observations and objections

The Thames Barrier shuts to stop the sea flooding London. Without it, London would be flooded once every 1000 years causing £80 billion of damage. The barrier halves this risk. However, global warming is raising sea levels. In the 1980s the barrier shut 4 times, 35 times in the 1990s and 80 times in the 2000s. By 2030, the barrier is not expected to reduce the flood risk below today's risk.

Increasing carbon dioxide (CO_2) levels in the atmosphere cause global warming. CO_2 absorbs heat and so stops the Earth losing so much heat into the atmosphere. Scientists collect data about CO_2 levels and global temperatures to create computer models that predict the effects of increasing CO_2 levels.

Figure A: The Thames Barrier cost £1.5 billion (at today's prices).

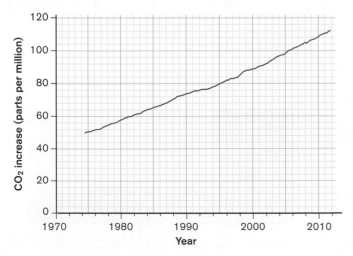

Figure B: CO_2 levels above a mountain in Hawaii.

To make predictions using the computer models, scientists need to forecast what will happen to the populations of different countries and how much energy those countries will need in the future. This is difficult to do and so they invent different 'scenarios' of what might happen in the future. Each scenario is then fed into the computer model. The chart on the left of Figure C shows the extra CO_2 that would be added to the atmosphere in different scenarios. The graph on the right then shows the predicted effects on the Earth's temperature for three of those scenarios (A2, A1B and B1).

Extra CO_2 and other greenhouse gases in the atmosphere in 2030 compared with 2000.

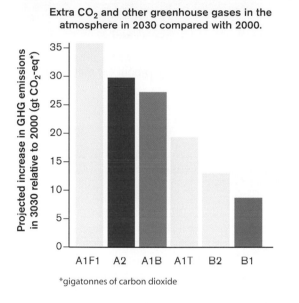

*gigatonnes of carbon dioxide

Yearly mean global surface increase in temperature for different scenarios (compared with the mean value for 1980–1999 (°C))

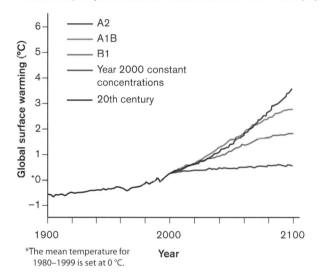

*The mean temperature for 1980–1999 is set at 0 °C.

Figure C: Computer model predictions of global temperature rises with different increases in CO_2.

QUESTIONS

1 Draw a graph or chart to display the times the Thames Barrier has shut. ▶▶ **S38**

2 Explain why two different types of chart/graph are used in Figure C. ▶▶ **S31, S33, S50**

3 Suggest what the term 'computer model' means. ▶▶ **S40**

4 a Scientists used Figure B to create a model for global warming. Suggest an advantage of using one set of data. ▶▶ **S11**
  b Suggest a disadvantage. ▶▶ **S12**
  c From where do you think CO_2 data should be collected for computer models? ▶▶ **S12**

5 Use Figure B to calculate the yearly rate of increase of CO_2 levels. ▶▶ **S35**

6 Calculate the percentage probability of London flooding: ▶▶ **S29**
  a today, without the Thames Barrier
  b today, with the Thames Barrier
  c in 2030, if there were no Thames Barrier

7 London's flood risk is quite low. Suggest why the Thames Barrier was built. ▶▶ **S45, S50**

8 Explain whether this page would make a good magazine article or not.
  ▶▶ **QWC** **S47, S48, S49, S50**

Long Answer Grade Booster

★★★ justifies views
★★★ describes how problems should be solved
★★★ identifies pros and cons

Airbags reduce the risk of injury in a car crash. One study of 2864 crashes discovered that 139 people suffered serious kidney injuries. Of these, 96 were in cars without airbags and 43 were in cars with airbags.

In a crash a sensor circuit produces a spark. In some airbag systems, the spark causes sodium azide (NaN_3) to decompose, releasing nitrogen gas. Sodium azide is very poisonous and can cause people to stop breathing. So, it is kept in a strong container.

$$2NaN_3 \rightarrow 2Na + 3N_2$$

An airbag needs a certain pressure of gas in it. It must not be too hard or it will hurt the driver but it won't work if it's too soft. Figure B shows the result of an investigation to find out what pressures were generated in different sizes of airbag.

Figure A: An airbag inflates in about 30 milliseconds.

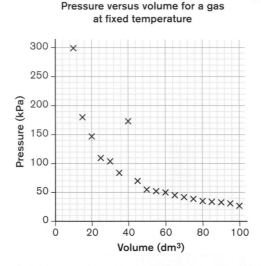

Pressure versus volume for a gas at fixed temperature

Figure B: The pressure of gas produced by 130 g NaN_3 in different sizes of airbag.

QUESTIONS

1 How many seconds does it take for an airbag to inflate? ▶▶ **S6**

2 Write out the equation above in words, starting 'Two units of sodium azide...' ▶▶ **S26**

3 a A trial run was done for the pressure investigation. State three reasons why. ▶▶ **S23, S50**

b State two control variables used. ▶▶ **S13**

4 a On the graph, which result would you check again and why? ▶▶ **S19**

b What is the relationship between pressure and volume? ▶▶ **HIGHER** **S35**

c How would you manipulate the data to draw a straight line graph? ▶▶ **HIGHER** **S35**

5 130 g of NaN_3 is used for an airbag that needs 35 kPa of pressure. A cylinder-shaped bag is 26 cm tall and 58 cm in diameter. Is it the right size? Explain your answer. ▶▶ **S8**

6 Airbags are compulsory by law in some countries. Describe two factors that would be considered when deciding whether to make airbags compulsory in the UK. ▶▶ **S46, S50**

7 Discuss the fitting of airbags in cars. Think about the benefits, drawbacks and risks. ▶▶ **QWC** **S24, S27, S44, S49, S50**

Long Answer Grade Booster

★★★ risk reduction is evaluated

★★★ benefits, drawbacks and risk-reduction methods described

★★★ one benefit, drawback and risk-reduction method stated

C9 AVOGADRO'S BIG IDEA

Jöns Berzelius (1779–1848), an influential Swedish chemist, believed that particles combined using 'electrical force', so two oxygen atoms had the same charge and could not join in pairs.

In France, Joseph Gay-Lussac (1778–1850) showed that volumes of gases reacted in ratios of whole numbers. So, two volumes of hydrogen and one of oxygen reacted to form two volumes of water. This was difficult to understand (see Figure A).

A little known Italian, Amedeo Avogadro (1776–1856), then had some ideas:

* equal volumes of different gases contained the same number of 'particles'
* 'particles' could split (e.g. oxygen might have two joined particles).

Avogadro used his ideas to calculate the mass of oxygen particles compared to hydrogen particles. His ideas were ignored until Stanislao Cannizzaro (1826–1910) used them to accurately calculate the masses of atoms of different elements and did experiments to show that the calculations were correct. Avogadro's name is now used to describe 6.02×10^{23} particles – Avogadro's number or one 'mole'.

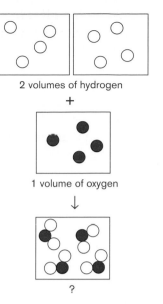

2 volumes of hydrogen
+
1 volume of oxygen
↓
?

Figure A: Chemists had trouble explaining Gay-Lussac's observations because if you joined up all the particles you got only one volume of water, not two.

QUESTIONS

1 $96 \, cm^3$ of hydrogen reacts with $32 \, cm^3$ nitrogen. What ratio is this? ▶▶ **S27**

2 Avogadro used 1.10359 for the density of oxygen and 0.07321 for hydrogen.
  a Suggest a unit used to measure density today. ▶▶ **S6, S9**
  b Give these figures to three significant figures. ▶▶ **S18**
  c From these figures Avogadro calculated how much heavier an oxygen particle was, compared to hydrogen (oxygen's 'relative atomic mass'). Calculate this figure. ▶▶ **S27, S50**
  d Use the information from the periodic table on page 126 to compare Avogadro's answer to today's figure. ▶▶ **S30, S50**

3 Redraw Figure A to show what we now think happens in this reaction. ▶▶ **S40**

4 Draw a flow chart to show how Avogadro's ideas about how to calculate the masses of particles (compared with hydrogen particles) became a theory. ▶▶ **S1**

5 Suggest why Avogadro's ideas were ignored. ▶▶ **S43, S50**

6 At 'standard temperature and pressure' a mole of any gas always has the same volume. Use the information in the table to draw a chart/graph to calculate this volume of gas per mole. ▶▶ **S30, S34, S35, S50**

Number of moles	2	4	6	8	10
Volume (dm³)	46	90	130	180	225

Long Answer Grade Booster

★★★ all working clearly shown

★★★ accurate chart/graph with calculation

★★★ appropriate chart/graph drawn and labelled

When athletes have sprains they often put a 'cold pack' on the affected area to reduce the swelling. Some cold packs use chemicals that cause energy to be taken out of the surroundings when they dissolve in water.

An experiment was done to test the idea that some chemicals are better than others for use in cold packs. 25 cm³ of water was added to a mixture of chemical powders and the drop in temperature was recorded. The balance could measure down to 0.1 g and the thermometer could measure down to 0.1 °C. The results are in the table. It was concluded that 5 g of sodium nitrate was best for making a cold pack.

Figure A: This cold pack contains ammonium chloride. The pack is twisted to release water into the chemical. As the ammonium chloride dissolves it becomes very cold.

Mass of ammonium chloride (g)	Mass of sodium nitrate (g)	Change in temperature (°C)		
		1st try	2nd try	3rd try
2.5	2	8.0	7.4	7.4
2.5	3	9.2	7.9	8.1
2.5	4	15.2	9.1	9.3
2.5	5	11.8	10.2	10.4
2.5	6	10.3	10.1	10.2

Figure B: Ammonium chloride is harmful if breathed in. Sodium nitrate is harmful if swallowed and irritates the skin.

QUESTIONS

1 What was the resolution of the thermometer? ▶▶ **S17**

2 Suggest two ways in which the risks of using these chemicals can be reduced. ▶▶ **S24, S50**

3 a Identify the most anomalous result. ▶▶ **S19, S50**

  b Calculate the mean temperature changes. ▶▶ **S20, S50**

  c Draw an appropriate graph or chart to show the means. ▶▶ **S38**

  d What correlation does your graph/chart show? ▶▶ **S15**

4 Suggest two control variables for this investigation. ▶▶ **S13, S50**

5 Suggest what needs to be done to be more certain of the conclusion given. ▶▶ **S39, S50**

6 What hypothesis did this investigation want to test? ▶▶ **QWC** **S3**

7 Evaluate this investigation. ▶▶ **QWC** **S42, S49, S50**

Long Answer Grade Booster

★★★ justifies opinions on the validity of the investigation

★★★ describes strengths and weaknesses of the investigation

★★★ comments on the quality of the data

P1 COLD FUSION

Nuclear power uses heat produced by splitting atoms to generate electricity. It doesn't produce smoke or carbon dioxide but does produce radioactive waste (which can cause cancers).

Fusing atoms together produces heat but little radioactive waste. Fusion occurs in the Sun, at about 15 million °C. In 1989, scientists were trying to make fusion happen at room temperature. Stanley Pons and Martin Fleischmann were writing a paper about the experiment they had done. So was Steven E. Jones. They all agreed to send their two papers to *Nature* on the same day.

Pons and Fleischmann didn't wait for publication and gave a press conference, saying they could cause 'cold fusion' of deuterium atoms but didn't know how it worked. If deuterium atoms fuse, the accepted theory says that heat and helium gas are produced, along with neutrons, protons or gamma rays. Pons and Fleischmann only measured heat increase and there was no control experiment. Other scientists could not replicate their work nor detect helium, protons, neutrons or gamma rays.

Figure A: A nuclear explosion in Chernobyl in 1986 caused up to 270 000 cancer cases.

Palladium is a metal. They used different volumes of palladium in their experiments.

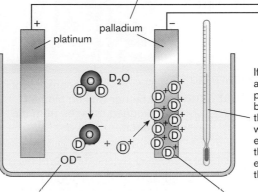

If the deuterium atoms fuse in the palladium, heat will be released and the temperature will rise. The heat energy will be more than the electrical energy put into the device.

Deuterium is a type of 'heavy hydrogen', which can be used to make 'heavy water' (D_2O). They added different amounts of this to the apparatus during their experiments.

When electricity is passed through the solution, deuterium is released from the D_2O and is absorbed by the palladium.

Figure B: Pons and Fleischmann's experiment.

QUESTIONS

1 Suggest a benefit and a drawback of nuclear power. ▸▸ S44, S50

2 a What hypothesis did Pons and Fleischmann test? ▸▸ QWC S3

 b Suggest two predictions made by this hypothesis. ▸▸ QWC S3, S50

3 Write out 15 million °C in standard form. ▸▸ HIGHER S10

4 Explain why a paper should be published before press conferences are given. ▸▸ S43, S50

5 a Suggest how Pons and Fleischmann acted unethically. ▸▸ S46, S50

 b Give two reasons why most scientists don't believe their results. ▸▸ S1, S3, S14, S22

6 Pons and Fleischmann may have over-estimated the amount of heat energy they produced because they didn't stir the liquid. Suggest how. ▸▸ S39, S50

7 Explain what a control is and suggest some controls for Pons and Fleischmann's experiment. ▸▸ QWC S14, S49, S50

Long Answer Grade Booster

★★★ explains why a control is needed, with correct suggestions

★★★ describes what a control is, with a correct suggestion

★★★ states the need for a control, with a suggestion

According to legend, Galileo Galilei (1564–1642), dropped two masses from the top of the leaning tower of Pisa. One mass was ten times heavier than the other but they hit the ground at the same time.

The legendary experiment tested Galileo's idea that gravity acts on all objects equally. This means that all dropped objects accelerate towards the Earth at the same rate. Galileo's results showed that Aristotle (384 BCE–322 BCE) was wrong when he claimed that a mass that was ten times heavier would fall ten times faster.

Figure A: Historians doubt whether Galileo himself dropped masses from the tower.

However, some objects are slowed by air. There is no air on the Moon and so in 1971 an astronaut dropped a hammer and a feather at the same time. Both objects hit the ground together.

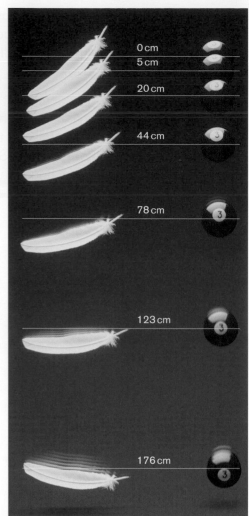

Figure B: A feather and a ball dropped at the same time in a vacuum (no air at all), with an image taken every 0.1 seconds.

QUESTIONS

1 Is the data from Galileo's experiment quantitative or qualitative? ▶▶ **S5**

2 Convert 0.1 seconds into milliseconds. ▶▶ **S6**

3 Use the word 'reproducible' to explain why we think Galileo's idea is correct. ▶▶ **S22, S50**

4 a Calculate the mean speed of the ball in Figure B using $s = \dfrac{d}{t}$. ▶▶ **S9, S50**

b Suggest why Galileo was not able to calculate the objects' speeds. ▶▶ **S17, S50**

5 a Calculate time squared (t^2) for each position of the ball in Figure B. Present your answer as a table. ▶▶ **S7, S30**

b Draw a scatter graph with a line of best fit for distance against t^2. ▶▶ **S34**

c Describe the relationship shown on your graph. ▶▶ **S34, S50**

d Use the information in your graph to calculate the constant of proportionality. ▶▶ **S35**

6 Draw a flow chart to show how Galileo's idea has become a theory. ▶▶ **S1**

Long Answer Grade Booster

★★★ shows how the theory has been tested

★★★ correctly uses and illustrates the terms hypothesis and theory

★★★ shows how Galileo's idea was tested

P3 PET SCANS

In the 1920s, Paul Dirac (1902–1984) developed a mathematical equation to model what happens to negatively charged electrons in different situations. His equation only worked if electrons with positive charges also existed. So, he predicted 'positrons', which were found in 1932 and are used in PET scanners.

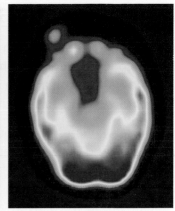

A CT scan   A PET scan

Figure A: Different scans of a person's head. The scans are from a study to work out how good PET scanners are at detecting eye cancers.

In a PET scan, a radioactive version of a compound that your body uses (e.g. glucose) is injected. The compound, called a tracer, produces positrons. The scanner detects where the positrons are produced and displays the results on a screen.

Tracers are very expensive and need to be made close-by, so only some hospitals have PET scanners. A scan increases the risk of cancer by 1 in 10 000. The risk is greater if you are still growing, so children and pregnant woman don't usually have PET scans.

QUESTIONS

1 a What scientific question did Paul Dirac ask?
▶ **S2**

b What prediction did his model make?
▶ **QWC S3**

2 The table shows more results from the study into PET scans and eye cancers.

Patient number	Average radius of cancer (mm)	PET scan detected the cancer?
1	4.63	No
2	5.25	No
3	8.00	Yes
4	5.50	No
5	9.25	Yes
6	9.00	Yes
7	7.75	Yes
8	8.00	Yes
9	6.25	Yes
10	3.25	No

a Assume that a cancer is a sphere. Calculate the volume of the cancer in each patient. Give your answers to three significant figures.
▶ **S7, S8, S18**

b Why are the volumes you calculated only estimates? ▶ **S11, S40**

c This was a small study, like a trial run. Explain one reason why scientists use trial runs. ▶ **S23, S50**

d What range of cancer radii would you choose to test to work out a better idea of what the resolution of a PET scanner is for detected eye cancers? ▶ **S17, S20**

3 Discuss the use of PET scans. Think about the benefits, drawbacks and risks.
▶ **QWC S24, S27, S41, S44, S50**

Long Answer Grade Booster

★★★ benefits, drawbacks and risks explained using examples

★★★ benefits, drawbacks and risks described

★★★ one benefit, drawback and risk stated

Ig® Nobel Prizes are given to scientists whose research makes people laugh and then makes them think. Dr Lianne Parkin won a prize in 2010 for investigating the effect of wearing socks outside shoes in icy conditions.

Dr Parkin and her team found 30 volunteers on an icy footpath, and gave each an envelope at random. Half the envelopes contained the word 'socks' and the other half contained the phrase 'no socks'. Those in the 'socks' group were given 'acrylic blend work socks' to put on, *over* their footwear. The people were timed as they walked down the path and asked how slippery they thought the path was on a scale of 1–5.

One person didn't complete the task. One person had a sock flapping off her shoe, creating a hazard, but her results were included. During planning, Dr Parkin thought about using the world's steepest road but decided this would be 'ethically … unwise'.

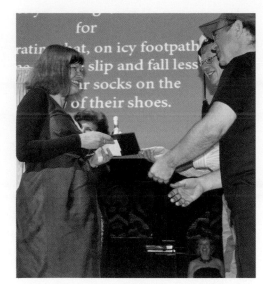

Figure A: Dr Parkin receiving her award from Prof. Sheldon Glashow.

Group	Number of ...		Age range	Slipperiness ratings (5 is most slippery)	Times taken to descend the slope (s)
	men	women			
Socks	7	7	19–58	1, 1, 1, 1, 1.5, 2, 1.5, 1, 1, 1, 1, 3, 1, 5	23.9, 27.2, 32.0, 42.4, 38.9, 29.2, 45.0, 26.1, 40.9, 43.0, 48.3, 31.9, 55.0, 44.0
No socks	10	5	18–70	1.5, 2, 2, 1, 1.5, 2, 2.5, 4, 4, 3, 4, 4, 5, 5, 2	29.2, 32.0, 35.4, 48.0, 29.0, 27.8, 30.8, 44.4, 48.4, 48.4, 29.9, 69.4, 39.7, 49.0, 33.1

QUESTIONS

1 Give one variable that was controlled and one that was not. ▶▶ **S13**

2 a Which group was the control? Explain your reasoning. ▶▶ **S14, S50**

 b Why was a control group used? ▶▶ **S14**

3 What is the most anomalous reading in the times taken to descend? ▶▶ **S19**

4 a Calculate means for the slipperiness ratings and times for both groups. Use all the results. ▶▶ **S20, S50**

 b Why are means calculated? ▶▶ **S20**

 c Show the means on two appropriate graphs or charts. ▶▶ **S38**

5 Explain why using the steep street would have been 'ethically unwise'. ▶▶ **S46, S50**

6 Why is it important that the groups were chosen randomly? ▶▶ **S12**

7 Suggest another question that could be answered by a similar investigation. ▶▶ **S2, S50**

8 Identify the hazards mentioned on this page and explain how the risks should be reduced, producing an argument in support of your ideas. ▶▶ **QWC** **S24, S41, S50**

Long Answer Grade Booster

★★★ explains evidence for risk reduction as part of an argument

★★★ correctly refers to hazards, risks and risk reduction

★★★ identifies a danger

High-pitch deterrent devices (HPDDs) emit high-pitched sounds that only younger people can hear. They can stop people hanging around certain areas.

You hear high-frequency sound waves as high-pitched sounds. The frequency of a wave is measured in hertz (Hz). Loudness can be measured in decibels (dB).

A shopkeeper wanted to find the best pitch and loudness settings for an HPDD. Lucy (aged 14) and her dad Brian (aged 47) agreed to help. They listened to different frequencies. The loudness of each frequency was increased until they heard the sounds.

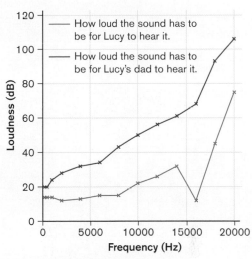

Figure B: The shopkeeper's results.

Figure A: An HPDD.

QUESTIONS

1 What is 12 000 Hz in kilohertz? ▶ **S6**

2 Which measurement needs checking? Explain your choice. ▶ **S19**

3 What correlation does the graph show? ▶ **S15**

4 The loudest sound wave Brian heard had a pressure of 2 000 000 μPa.
   a What does the μPa mean? ▶ **S6**
   b Why do scientists use symbols? ▶ **S26**
   c Convert this figure into standard form. ▶ **HIGHER S10**
   d The loudest sound wave Lucy heard had a pressure of 5×10^3 μPa. In μPa, how much less was this pressure compared to the one above? Show your working in standard form. ▶ **HIGHER S10**

5 a An HPDD can be set to 8 or 17.4 kHz, and 40, 60 or 100 dB. Explain which settings you would recommend. ▶ **S6, S33, S50**
   b Should the shopkeeper have used secondary data? Explain your reasoning. ▶ **S25, S50**

6 Brian said "The experiment shows that adults can't hear sound waves over 25 000 Hz." Is this valid? Explain your reasoning. ▶ **S21, S39, S50**

7 A shop is thinking about installing an HPDD to stop younger people hanging around outside it. However, some people have said it is wrong to use a device that affects all young people. Explain how you would go about deciding for or against installing an HPDD. ▶ **QWC S46, S49, S50**

Long Answer Grade Booster
★★★ explains the full range of evidence needed
★★★ describes some other evidence needed
★★★ states some simple factors to take into account

Distances in space can be measured in degrees (like angles). Such a measurement is the number of degrees you turn when moving from looking at one point to another. 1/60th of a degree is called an arcminute and an arcsecond is 1/60th of an arcminute. Modern telescopes can measure fractions of arcseconds.

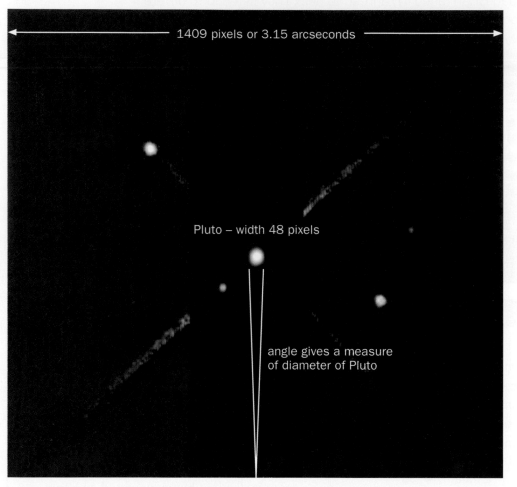

Figure A: Pluto as seen using a telescope in America. Its diameter can be expressed in arcseconds.

The smallest measureable distance in the 16th century was about half an arcminute. At this time Nicolaus Copernicus (1473–1543) proposed that the Earth went around the Sun, not the other way round. This explained why, during a year, planets got brighter and dimmer and why some planets appeared to travel backwards.

Copernicus' idea predicted parallax for some stars (see Figure B). No one could observe this and so many thought that Copernicus was wrong. A star's parallax was first observed in 1838 (with an angle of 0.314 arcseconds).

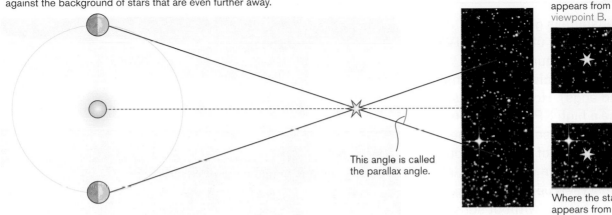

Viewpoint A. Looking at the star it appears in a certain position against the background of stars that are even further away.

Viewpoint B. The Earth has now moved on its orbit around the Sun and so the star appears in different place against the background of other stars.

This angle is called the parallax angle.

Where the star appears from viewpoint B.

Where the star appears from viewpoint A.

Not to scale

Figure B: Parallax would not happen if the Earth didn't move position.

QUESTIONS

1 a What 16th century evidence supported Copernicus' hypothesis? ▶▶ **S3**

b Explain how Copernicus' hypothesis became a theory. ▶▶ **S4, S50**

2 Why wasn't parallax of a star observed by Copernicus? ▶▶ **S17**

3 How much of a degree is one arcsecond? Show your working. ▶▶ **S27**

4 a Use the information in Figure A to calculate the width of Pluto in arcseconds.

b Show your answer as a fraction.

c Give your answer to part a in arcminutes. ▶▶ **S27, S50**

5 a The table shows parallax angles of various stars and their distances from the Sun. Plot the data on an appropriate chart or graph. ▶▶ **S38**

b How are the two variables related? ▶▶ **HIGHER** **S35**

6 a Parallaxes are now measured by satellites. Before this, all parallaxes had been overestimated. What effect would this have on the distances? ▶▶ **HIGHER** **S16, S35**

b What sort of error was this? ▶▶ **S17**

7 Explain how the observations on this page confirmed Copernicus' theory. ▶▶ **QWC** **S43, S49, S50**

Long Answer Grade Booster

★★★ explains expected observations if Copernicus was wrong

★★★ describes observations using Copernicus' theory

★★★ identifies some observations

Parallax (arcseconds)	0.77	0.55	0.37	0.27	0.23	0.22	0.21	0.20
Distance (light-years)	4.2	6.0	8.7	12.0	14.3	15.1	15.8	15.9

Sunshine is good for you because its ultraviolet (UV) rays help your skin make vitamin D (also found in fish and eggs). However, you should use a high SPF sunscreen if in the sun for some time. The SPF is the ratio of how long you can be in the sun wearing sunscreen before burning, compared to without sunscreen.

Figure A: Sunscreens display SPF (sun protection factor) numbers.

Sunscreens protect you against ultraviolet B rays, which cause sunburn. UVA rays are not stopped by all sunscreens but can damage cells, even though they don't cause sunburn.

An investigation was done to see if high SPF sunscreens protect skin better than low ones. A type of white bead goes purple when exposed to UVB rays. 21 beads were placed on a card and covered with colourless plastic film. Different sunscreens were smeared on the film over each bead. The card was then placed under a UVB lamp.

SPF	Time taken to go purple (s)		
	Bead 1	Bead 2	Bead 3
4	70	75	74
8	131	134	134
15	276	278	274
30	688	542	798
50	1949	1900	1896

QUESTIONS

1 a How can you reduce the risk of sunburn? ▶ S24

b People are more likely to use sunscreens if warned about cancer than if warned about sunburn. Suggest why. ▶ S45, S50

2 a What is the independent (input) variable in the investigation? ▶ S13

b State two variables that should have been controlled. ▶ S13

3 Jack can have 10 minutes in the sun before he starts to burn. How long could he have when using a 15 SPF sunscreen? ▶ S27

4 Which set of readings in the table is the least precise? ▶ S16, S30

5 a Calculate the means for each set of readings in the table. ▶ S20, S50

b Plot your means on an appropriate chart or graph. ▶ S38

c What correlation does your graph show? ▶ S15

6 Evaluate the investigation. ▶ S42, S50

7 Using this page and page 20 (B9), explain whether or not you think sunbathing is a good idea. ▶ QWC S41, S48, S49, S50

Long Answer Grade Booster

★★★ synthesises information

★★★ uses a lot of information from both pages

★★★ states a reason for and against sunbathing

P8 SPEED LIMITS

'Average speed cameras' enforce a speed limit of 50 mph (80 km/h) at motorway roadworks. Two cameras, a certain distance apart, take photos marked with times of every car. A computer calculates the mean speed for each car using speed = distance ÷ time.

The speed limit on most motorways is normally 70 mph (113 km/h) but some want this to be higher.

> **HIGHER** They claim that the limit should be set using the speed that the 85th percentile of drivers would drive at on a motorway (about 80 mph).

Others disagree and say that raising the limit would encourage people to drive faster, increasing the risks of serious injury (data in the table is from a 1994 study).

Figure A: Average speed cameras.

Speed change after impact (mph)	1–10	11–20	21–30	31–40	41–50	50+
Probability of serious injury	0.01	0.026	0.111	0.279	0.406	0.543

Figure B: Graph used by supporters of raising the speed limit based on studies carried out in the 1950s and 60s.

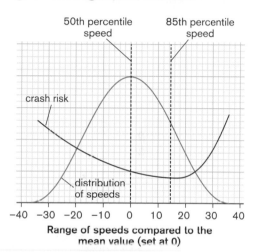

QUESTIONS

1 a Which units for speed on this page are SI units? ▶▶ **S6**

b The units for speed are compound units. What does this mean? ▶▶ **S9**

2 a The times on two photos from speed cameras seven miles apart for one car are 14:03:02, 14:10:4 (hours:minutes:seconds). How long in seconds did the car take? ▶▶ **S6**

b What was the car's speed in mph? ▶▶ **S40**

c Cars going over a certain mean speed are sent a fine. This speed is 10% over the speed limit + 2 mph. Will the car driver be fined? ▶▶ **S27**

3 A car travels at 40 km/h for 15 minutes. How far will it go? ▶▶ **HIGHER** **S40**

4 What is the percentage risk of serious injury if the change in speed after impact is 31–40 mph? ▶▶ **S29, S45**

5 What is meant by the 85th percentile? ▶▶ **HIGHER** **S28**

6 Display the data in the table on a suitable graph or chart. ▶▶ **S38**

7 Imagine this page was a magazine article. Evaluate the article. ▶▶ **QWC** **S47, S48, S49, S50**

Long Answer Grade Booster

★★★ evaluation indicates what additional evidence there should be

★★★ opinion about the article backed up with evidence

★★★ statement about how good the article is

Dan wanted to see if the amount of light reflected from a board could be used to measure its distance accurately. To detect the light, he had to decide between using a light dependent resistor (LDR) or a photodiode. During pre-tests he found that the LDR was more sensitive. He set up two circuits; one containing an LDR and one with a switch and a bulb. The circuits were separated by a piece of wood.

When the board was 1 m away from the bulb, he measured the voltage across the resistor in the LDR circuit. He measured the voltage at other distances and plotted Figure B.

He then placed the board at other distances. He measured the voltage and used this to predict the distance of the board, before using a ruler to measure the actual distance. His results are shown in the table. Dan concluded that measuring distances like this was possible but not very accurate.

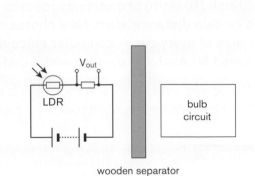

Figure A: Dan's set up.

Position	Distance predicted by Figure B (m)	Actual distance (m)
1	0.22	0.21
2	0.46	0.43
3	0.75	0.79

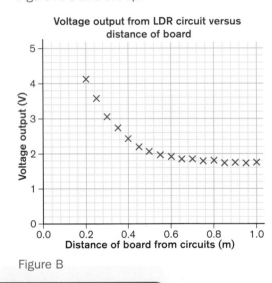

Figure B

QUESTIONS

1 a What trial run did Dan do? ▶▶ **S23**
  b State two reasons for doing a trial run. ▶▶ **S23, S50**

2 What range did Dan choose for the independent variable? ▶▶ **S13, S20, S34**

3 a The 'bulb circuit' had a battery, bulb and switch. Draw a circuit diagram. ▶▶ **S26**
  b Draw an appropriate diagram to compare the components in the two circuits. ▶▶ **S38**

4 What is meant by 'the LDR was more sensitive' than the photodiode? ▶▶ **S17**

5 When the board was in 'Position 2', what would the voltage have been? ▶▶ **S34, S35**

6 a Calculate the percentage error for each predicted distance. This is the difference between the predicted and actual values compared with the actual value. ▶▶ **S27, S50**
  b What sort of error is this? ▶▶ **S17**
  c Suggest one way in which this error might have been caused. ▶▶ **S17, S50**

7 Evaluate this investigation. ▶▶ **QWC** **S42, S49, S50**

Long Answer Grade Booster

★★★ justifies opinions on the validity of the investigation

★★★ describes strengths and weaknesses of the investigation

★★★ comments on the quality of the data

The Large Hadron Collider (LHC) contains a 27 km long circular tunnel. Streams of protons or ions are accelerated in the tunnel and collide with one another. The protons can travel at just 3 m/s less than the speed of light.

Experiments in the LHC could help us find out what 'dark matter' is. In 1933 Fritz Zwicky (1898–1974) discovered that the mass of the stars seen in some galaxies was 160 times less than the accepted theory predicted. He proposed that the extra mass was there but you couldn't see it – it was 'dark'.

Figure A: The LHC cost £3 billion to build underground, near Geneva.

Scientists now think that 23% of the Universe is dark matter, 4.6% is particles and the rest is 'dark energy'. Dark energy cannot be detected at the moment but scientists use it to help explain why the Universe is expanding. Hopefully, the LHC will allow scientists to confirm whether it exists. Technology from LHC experiments may help improve many things, like medical scanning and the internet.

QUESTIONS

1 State two scientific questions that LHC scientists have asked. ▶▶ **S2, S50**

2 Draw an appropriate chart or graph to show what scientists think the Universe is made of. ▶▶ **S38**

3 a The speed of light is 2.99792458×10^8 m/s. To how many significant figures is this value? ▶▶ **S9, S18**

b How fast can protons travel in the LHC? Answer in standard form. ▶▶ **HIGHER S10**

c At this speed, how long will it take a proton to make one lap of the LHC? Use speed = distance/time and give your answer in standard form. ▶▶ **HIGHER S40, S10**

d What is the speed of light to one significant figure in m/ns? ▶▶ **S6, S18**

4 Suggest a benefit and a drawback of the LHC. ▶▶ **S44, S50**

5 a What hypothesis is used to explain why the Universe is expanding? ▶▶ **QWC S3**

b If LHC scientists find evidence for this, how will other scientists be involved in confirming it? ▶▶ **S43**

6 Draw a flow chart to show how Zwicky changed the theory of what the Universe was made of. ▶▶ **S1**

Long Answer Grade Booster

★★★ shows how the theory is built upon

★★★ correctly uses and illustrates the terms hypothesis and theory

★★★ draws a flow chart showing Zwicky's idea

The **scientific method** is a process (series of steps) that scientists use to show whether their ideas are correct or not. A man called Ibn al Haytham (born in Basra, which is now in Iraq, in 965) laid the foundations of this method. He is often called 'the first scientist' because he was the first thinker to test ideas using scientific experiments. Diagram B is a **flow chart** showing the steps in the scientific method.

Figure A: Ibn al Haytham (965–1039).

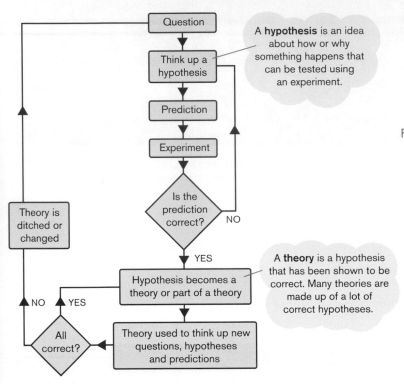

Question

A **hypothesis** is an idea about how or why something happens that can be tested using an experiment.

Think up a hypothesis

Prediction

Experiment

Is the prediction correct?   NO

Theory is ditched or changed

YES

Hypothesis becomes a theory or part of a theory

A **theory** is a hypothesis that has been shown to be correct. Many theories are made up of a lot of correct hypotheses.

NO   YES

All correct?

Theory used to think up new questions, hypotheses and predictions

Figure B: The scientific method.

Apply your skills ▶▶ **B3** ▶▶ **C9** ▶▶ **P1, P2, P10**

S2 SCIENTIFIC QUESTIONS

Scientific questions are questions that can be answered using information from experiments. Questions like 'Why do plants grow towards light?' or 'How do rainbows form?' are scientific questions.

Not all scientific questions have answers because we don't have enough good information. This may be because not enough experiments have been done yet or because the experiments are too expensive or are impossible to do with current technology.

Questions involving attitudes, **morals** or **ethics** are not scientific questions. For example, questions such as 'Should I go to the party?' and 'Why is blue the best colour?' are not scientific because you can't do experiments to answer them.

Apply your skills ▶▶ B9 ▶▶ C6 ▶▶ P3, P4, P10

Figure A: What if Newton had been a biologist?

S3 HYPOTHESES AND PREDICTIONS

To answer a scientific question a scientist will think up an idea about how or why something happens. This is a **hypothesis**. Scientists must think creatively since a hypothesis needs to explain the observations that led to the original question.

The phrase 'depends on' is useful when writing hypotheses. For example, the height of a plant *depends on* the amount of fertiliser it is given.

The hypothesis can be used to write a **prediction** about what will happen in a certain experiment when the hypothesis is tested. For example, *If* plant A is given twice as much fertiliser as plant B *then* plant A will grow taller.

A scientist will give reasons for thinking that a hypothesis and prediction are correct.

QWC Notice that:

- ✘ *'depends on'* can be useful when writing a hypothesis
- ✘ *'if ... then ...'* can be useful when writing a prediction

Apply your skills ▶▶ B2, B3, B4, B9 ▶▶ C2, C6, C10 ▶▶ P1, P3, P6, P10

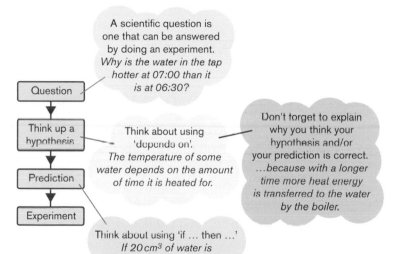

Figure A: The steps taken when testing an idea.

S4 THEORIES

A **hypothesis** that has been tested and shown to be correct (or not to be wrong) becomes a **theory**. So, a theory is an idea about how or why certain things happen, with **evidence** to support it.

Often a theory is produced from many hypotheses, that all have supporting evidence. For example, the **kinetic theory** has many hypotheses that deal with the different states of matter (solids, liquids, gases) when they are heated or squashed or hit etc..

A theory:

- allows predictions to be made
- explains all the observations
- may explain other observations that weren't thought to be linked to the theory
- can be tested

Apply your skills ▶▶ **B3** ▶▶ **C2, C6** ▶▶ **P6**

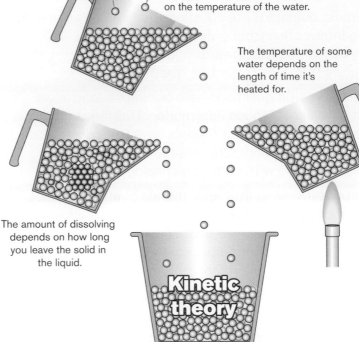

The speed of evaporation depends on the temperature of the water.

The temperature of some water depends on the length of time it's heated for.

The amount of dissolving depends on how long you leave the solid in the liquid.

Figure A: The kinetic theory contains many hypotheses.

S5 QUALITATIVE AND QUANTITATIVE DATA

Evidence is usually in the form of **data** (numbers or words that can be organised to give information). When data is given as numbers it comes with something telling you what the numbers mean (e.g. a unit of measurement, or percentage). Numbers with meanings are **values**. '5cm' is a value but '5' is not because you don't know what the 5 refers to.

Data in number form is quantitative data and there are two forms: **continuous** and **discrete**. **Continuous data** is where each value can be any number between two limits. **Discrete data** is where a value can only be one of a limited choice of numbers.

Data not in number form is **qualitative** or **categoric** data (data put into categories). **Name Check!** Don't confuse quantitative and qualitative. Numbers come in 'quantities' and so they are **quantitative** data.

Apply your skills ▶▶ **B2, B5** ▶▶ **C5** ▶▶ **P2**

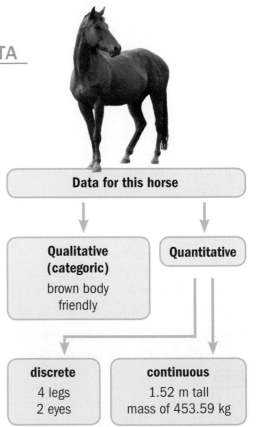

Data for this horse

Qualitative (categoric)
brown body
friendly

Quantitative

discrete
4 legs
2 eyes

continuous
1.52 m tall
mass of 453.59 kg

Figure A: The different types of data.

It's useful if everyone uses the same system for measurements.
All scientists use the 'Système International' or **SI system**. Five basic
units in this system are:

Quantity	Unit name	Symbol
length	metre	m
mass	gram	g
time	second	s
temperature	degree Celsius or kelvin	°C or K
current	ampere, amp	A

Additions are put at the front of the units to make them bigger or smaller:

Name addition	Symbol addition	meaning (words)	meaning (numbers)	meaning (standard form)
nano-	n	one thousand millionth	0.000000001	$\times 10^{-9}$
micro-	μ	one millionth	0.000001	$\times 10^{-6}$
milli-	m	one thousandth	0.001	$\times 10^{-3}$
centi-	c	one hundredth	0.01	$\times 10^{-2}$
deci-	d	one tenth	0.1	$\times 10^{-1}$
kilo-	k	× one thousand	1000	$\times 10^{3}$
mega-	M	× one million	1 000 000	$\times 10^{6}$
giga-	G	× one thousand million	1 000 000 000	$\times 10^{9}$
tera-	T	× one million million	1 000 000 000 000	$\times 10^{12}$

Other units are formed from the basic units in the first table above:

Quantity	Example units
area	m^2
volume	m^3
density	g/m^3
speed, velocity	m/s
	km/h
acceleration	m/s^2
momentum	kg m/s
force	N (newton)
pressure	N/m^2
	$1\,N/m^2 = 1\,Pa$ (pascal)
information	B (byte)

Quantity	Example units
power	W (watt)
energy	J (joule)
	Wh (watt hour)
frequency	Hz (hertz)
power of a lens	dioptre
potential difference	V (volt)
resistance	Ω (ohm)
astronomical distance	ly (light-year) pc (parsec)
gravitational field strength	N/kg
radiation dose	Sv (sievert)

Apply your skills ▶▶ **B5, B10** ▶▶ **C2, C3, C4, C6, C8, C9** ▶▶ **P2, P5, P8, P10**

S7 INDEX FORM

Some SI units are formed from multiplying one unit a number of times. For example, the **area** of a rectangle is worked out by multiplying its length by its width. If both measurements are in metres the unit for area will be 'square metres', which just means 'metres multiplied by metres'. We show the number of times that 'metres' have been multiplied together by using a **power** or **index** Name Check! , which is a number written after and above the unit symbol: m². Figure A shows another example.

Numbers can also have indices. For example, 5^2 means 5 multiplied by itself 2 times (or 5×5). This is said as 'five squared'. 5^3 means $5 \times 5 \times 5$ and is said as 'five cubed'.

Apply your skills ▶▶ **B1, B5, B10** ▶▶ **C2** ▶▶ **P2, P3**

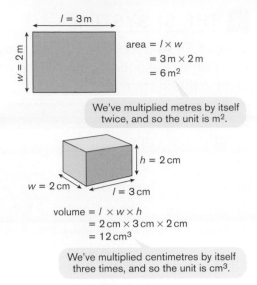

$l = 3\,\text{m}$
$w = 2\,\text{m}$

area = $l \times w$
= $3\,\text{m} \times 2\,\text{m}$
= $6\,\text{m}^2$

We've multiplied metres by itself twice, and so the unit is m².

$h = 2\,\text{cm}$
$w = 2\,\text{cm}$
$l = 3\,\text{cm}$

volume = $l \times w \times h$
= $2\,\text{cm} \times 3\,\text{cm} \times 2\,\text{cm}$
= $12\,\text{cm}^3$

We've multiplied centimetres by itself three times, and so the unit is cm³.

Figure A: Using index form saves time and is recognised by all scientists.

S8 CALCULATING PERIMETERS, AREAS AND VOLUMES

The diagram shows the ways in which the **perimeters**, **areas** and **volumes** of different shapes are calculated. Shapes that involve circles use a number called **pi** (written as π). This number never changes (it is a **mathematical constant**) and is the **circumference** of any circle divided by its **diameter**. Another way of saying this is that it is the **ratio** of any circle's circumference to its diameter.

Apply your skills ▶▶ **B1, B10** ▶▶ **C3, C8** ▶▶ **P3**

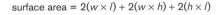
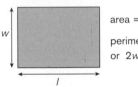
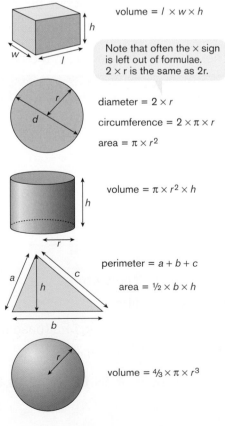

area = $l \times w$

perimeter = $w + w + l + l$
or $2w + 2l$

surface area = $2(w \times l) + 2(w \times h) + 2(h \times l)$

volume = $l \times w \times h$

Note that often the × sign is left out of formulae. $2 \times r$ is the same as 2r.

diameter = $2 \times r$

circumference = $2 \times \pi \times r$

area = $\pi \times r^2$

volume = $\pi \times r^2 \times h$

perimeter = $a + b + c$

area = $\tfrac{1}{2} \times b \times h$

volume = $\tfrac{4}{3} \times \pi \times r^3$

Figure A: Calculating perimeters, areas and volumes.

S9 COMPOUND MEASURES

Compound measures or **compound units** | Name Check! |
are formed from two or more other units. For example,
speed can use 'metres' and 'seconds'. These units are
shown together in a form that means 'the number of
metres travelled in one second' or 'metres per second'.
We show 'per' as a slash '/'. The unit is m/s.

> **HIGHER** Compound units can be written with a
> negative index (because it makes some calculations
> easier to do). A negative index means 1 divided by the
> positive power of the number. So, x^{-1} is the same as
> $1/x$, x^{-2} is $1/x^2$ and x^{-3} is $1/x^3$. For units, we can therefore
> write m/s as $m\ s^{-1}$ and g/cm^3 will become $g\ cm^{-3}$.

Apply your skills ▶▶ **B6, B10** ▶▶ **C3, C5, C6, C9** ▶▶ **P2, P8, P10**

S10 STANDARD FORM

HIGHER **Standard form** is a way of
writing very large or very small numbers
in a way that's easier to understand. To
write a large number in standard form
we shift the decimal point to the left
until we have a single digit (1 to 9). We
then write the number of places the
decimal point has shifted as a power of
10 ('10' with an index).

For example, 629 000 000 000 is 6.29×10^{11}.
The index is 11 because we shifted the
decimal point 11 places to the left. This is
the same as saying 6.29 multiplied by 10
$\times 10 \times 10 \times 10 \times 10 \times 10 \times 10 \times 10 \times 10 \times$
10×10. For very small numbers we do
the opposite and use a negative index.
For example 0.000 000 000 000 54 is
5.4×10^{-13}.

To add or subtract numbers in standard
form, you convert all the numbers to the
same power of 10. Then add or subtract
the main number and leave the index as
it is.

e.g. $3 \times 10^6 + 4 \times 10^7$
$= 3 \times 10^6 + 40 \times 10^6$
$= 43 \times 10^6$ or 4.3×10^7

$8 \times 10^8 - 3 \times 10^7$
$= 8 \times 10^8 - 0.3 \times 10^8 = 7.7 \times 10^8$

To divide in standard form, you divide
the big numbers and subtract the
indices.

e.g. $3 \times 10^6 \div 2 \times 10^5$
So, $3 \div 2 = 1.5$ and $6 - 5 = 1$.
The answer is 1.5×10^1 or 15.

To multiply, you multiply the main
numbers together and add the indices.

e.g. $4 \times 10^{-6} \times 8 \times 10^{-5}$
So, $4 \times 8 = 32$ and $-6 + -5 = -11$.

The answer comes out as 32×10^{-11}
which is 3.2×10^{-10}.

You'll usually use a calculator for these
calculations. To enter a number in
standard form, put in the first number,
then press EXP and then enter the index.

Apply your skills ▶▶ **B3, B5, B9** ▶▶ **C2** ▶▶ **P1, P5, P10**

Data can be collected in a variety of ways. For example, by doing an experiment or using a survey. In a survey you count the number of things that are of interest, without changing the conditions in which the things are found.

It often takes far too long to count things (e.g. the number of dandelions on playing fields). So scientists **estimate** the numbers, which means they use a rough calculation.

Estimating:
* saves time
* helps you to focus on the important parts of what you are doing

One way of estimating is to round figures up or down before doing a calculation. For example, if you wanted to know if £10 was enough to buy 3 coffees at £2.89 each you could say 'Well £2.89 is roughly £3 and 3 × £3 is £9, so I have enough'. That's a much easier calculation than 3 × £2.89 and you don't need to know the exact cost.

Scientists use the symbol ~ to show that a number is roughly right. For example, ~5 cm means 'roughly 5 centimetres'.

As well as rounding figures up or down to work out estimates, scientists use **extrapolation**. This means that you use part of some data (a **sample**) to estimate values outside the sample.

For example, to work out the number of red spots in Figure B you count the spots in a small sample area. Then calculate how many times bigger the whole area is compared with the sample area. Multiplying this number by the number of red spots counted gives an estimate of the total number of spots in the whole area.

Small coffee £1.11
Medium coffee £2.07
Large coffee £2.89

Three large coffees please.

Hang on, can we afford that?

Figure A: Estimating saves time.

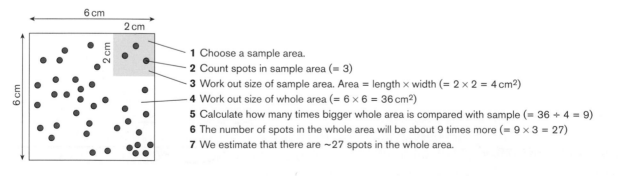

1 Choose a sample area.
2 Count spots in sample area (= 3)
3 Work out size of sample area. Area = length × width (= 2 × 2 = 4 cm²)
4 Work out size of whole area (= 6 × 6 = 36 cm²)
5 Calculate how many times bigger whole area is compared with sample (= 36 ÷ 4 = 9)
6 The number of spots in the whole area will be about 9 times more (= 9 × 3 = 27)
7 We estimate that there are ~27 spots in the whole area.

Figure B: By counting the spots in the small area and working out how many times that would be repeated, you can extrapolate how many red spots there are in total.

Apply your skills ▶▶ **B1, B10** ▶▶ **C7** ▶▶ **P3**

S12 SAMPLES AND BIAS

Bias is when evidence is distorted in one direction. Figure A will help you to understand this.

When you make estimates using samples it is quite easy to be biased. Look at Figure B. If you estimate the number of spots in the whole drawing using square A3, it comes out as 27 spots. If you use square A2, the estimate is 18 spots and with square C3 it is 72. The actual number is 38. All our estimates are biased – two have a bias below the real value and one has a bias above it.

You get better estimates, and reduce the effects of bias, if you take more samples. However, if you take too many samples it will take too long and defeat the object of taking samples! So for the big square, you might decide to estimate using three or four smaller sample squares from the grid. But how do you pick the squares to use?

For the best estimate, you need to choose samples at random. Doing this means that there is no bias caused by the experimenter because the experimenter does not make the choices. So to sample a field, a biologist would divide the field into a grid (as shown in Figure B) and then use a calculator or dice to generate random numbers to choose the squares to use.

Apply your skills ▶▶ B3, B7, B9, B10 ▶▶ C1, C5, C7 ▶▶ P4

Although the gun was aimed at the centre of the target, the bullets all ended up in the upper left of the target. There is bias. This might be due to the gun or to the person who is firing it.

Figure A: A way of thinking about bias.

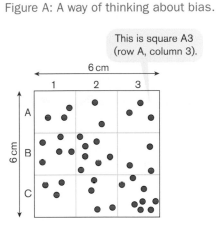

This is square A3 (row A, column 3).

Figure B: Small sample sizes can cause bias.

S13 VARIABLES AND FAIR TESTS

A variable is a factor that can change. In an investigation, the variable that is changed is the input variable or independent variable. **Name Check!** The variable you measure is the output variable or dependent variable. **Name Check!** The dependent variable *depends* on the independent variable.

In a hypothesis, if you can't work out which variable is which, try them both ways round. It only makes sense when the dependent variable comes first. For example:

✕ the length of time water is heated depends on its temperature rise ✗
✕ the temperature rise depends on the length of time the water is heated ✓

A control variable is a variable that could change during an investigation and affect the dependent variable. So you try to stop control variables changing. A fair test is when all these variables are successfully controlled.

Apply your skills ▶▶ B2, B4, B10 ▶▶ C1, C3, C8, C10 ▶▶ P4, P7, P9

Hypothesis: The current depends on the number of cells.
Prediction: If the number of cells is increased then the current will increase.

dependent variable: the current

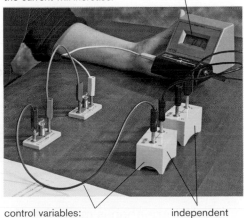

control variables:
i) same type of cell used
ii) rest of circuit kept the same

independent variable: the number of cells

Figure A: Different sorts of variables.

S14 CONTROLS

If a fair test is not possible (if there are too many control variables) a **control experiment** can be done, which has a **control** or **control group**. **Name Check!** A control is treated in the same way as the rest of the investigation but without the independent variable.

The control for the experiment in S13, would be a circuit without a cell (although we don't use controls if a fair test is possible).

Controls are used when investigating living things because they vary so much. The organisms are divided into groups, making sure that the groups are as similar to each other as possible. The independent variable is changed for the groups, but one group is a control. The results from the control make it easier to see if changes are only due to the independent variable.

Apply your skills ▶ **B2, B6, B9** ▶▶ **P1, P4**

Hypothesis: The time it takes for a headache to go depends on the amount of drug X taken.
Prediction: If more doses of drug X are taken then people will feel better more quickly.

Group A: 1 dose of drug X

Group A: 2 doses of drug X

Group A: 3 doses of drug X

Control: no drug X

Figure A: Controls are used in drug tests.

S15 CORRELATIONS

In many science experiments you want to observe how the independent (input) variable affects the dependent (output) variable. Since you want to see only the effect of the independent variable, all other variables need to be controlled.

A **correlation** is a link between changes in the independent variable (the cause) and changes in the dependent variable (the effect). If a dependent factor shows a steady change when you steadily change the independent factor, there is a correlation. There is also a correlation if something happens only if the independent variable is present.

A correlation can be strong or weak and positive or negative. A good way of showing a correlation is to use a **scattergram** or **scatter graph**. **Name Check!**

A correlation may be:
* **causal** – when the independent variable directly affects the dependent variable
* **due to association** – when both variables are affected by another variable
* **due to chance**

A causal correlation is more likely to be believed if there is a hypothesis that explains *how* it happens.

Apply your skills ▶ **B5, B7, B9, B10** ▶▶ **C4, C10** ▶▶ **P5, P7**

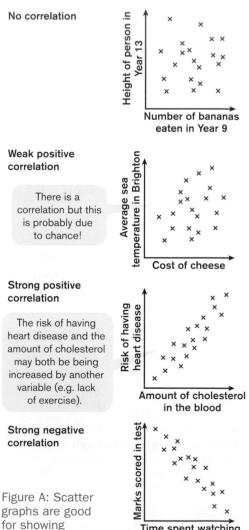

No correlation

Weak positive correlation

There is a correlation but this is probably due to chance!

Strong positive correlation

The risk of having heart disease and the amount of cholesterol may both be being increased by another variable (e.g. lack of exercise).

Strong negative correlation

Figure A: Scatter graphs are good for showing correlations.

S16 ACCURACY, BIAS AND PRECISION

Accuracy and **bias** are used to describe how close a measurement (or the average of a set of measurements) is to the true value. When using the term 'bias' we often talk of it as being in a certain direction (e.g. left, right, up, down).

Precision is how well grouped together a set of measurements are. If they are all close together, the measurements are described as being precise.

Apply your skills ⏭ **B6** ⏭ **C5** ⏭ **P7**

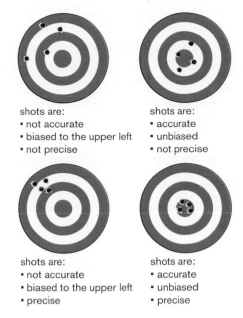

shots are:
- not accurate
- biased to the upper left
- not precise

shots are:
- accurate
- unbiased
- not precise

shots are:
- not accurate
- biased to the upper left
- precise

shots are:
- accurate
- unbiased
- precise

Figure A: Accuracy, bias and precision are different.

S17 ERRORS IN MEASUREMENTS

There will always be variation in a measurement if you repeat it. There is also a limit to how small a change any device can detect. This is its **resolution** or **sensitivity** `Name Check!` .

Look at Figure A. Using a measuring instrument with a higher resolution we can detect that one shot has not hit the very centre of the target. We cannot detect this with the lower resolution instrument – the shots are both in its most central square.

Human error happens when people make mistakes. It happens, even when measuring is done correctly, if an investigation is not carried out in the right way.

Random errors are when there is no pattern to the errors. It happens when repeated parts of an investigation are not done in exactly the same way. Measurements with random errors are usually not grouped together – they are not **precise**.

Systematic errors are caused when repeated parts of an investigation are done in the same way but that way is not correct. Measurements with systematic errors are often grouped but are not close to the real value – they are **precise** but not **accurate**.

Apply your skills ⏭ **B5** ⏭ **C1, C6, C10** ⏭ **P2, P3, P6, P9**

higher resolution – the instrument can detect the difference in position between the two shots

lower resolution – the instrument cannot detect the difference between the two shots

Figure A: Resolution.

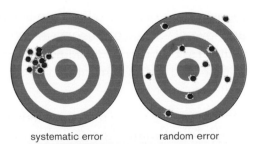

systematic error

random error

Figure B: Random and systematic errors.

S18 SIGNIFICANT FIGURES

Significant figures are the digits that show a value's accuracy. For example, a town's population is 10675 people. To two significant figures this is 11 000 (only two figures show the amount, the rest are zeros). 11 000 is a less accurate figure than 10675.

Less accurate measuring devices produce values with fewer significant figures, compared with more accurate devices.

When doing calculations, do not give your answer to more significant figures than the least accurate value that you started with.

Apply your skills ▶▶ **B1, B4** ▶▶ **C3, C9** ▶▶ **P3, P10**

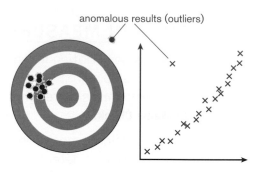

289687	To show this to 3 significant figures	0.0034523
289687	Count three digits from the left (starting from the first digit that is not a 0)	0.0034523
289687	Look at the digit after the significant figures. If it's 5 or greater, then increase the last significant figure by 1.	0.0034523
290000	Convert all the numbers to the right of your significant figures to 0.	0.0034500
290000 (3 sf)	State the number of significant figures in brackets. This step is not usually necessary.	0.00345 (3 sf)

Figure A: Changing significant figures.

S19 ANOMALOUS RESULTS AND OUTLIERS

An **anomalous result** or **outlier** `Name Check!` is a measurement that does not fit into the pattern of the other results. Anomalous results should be examined to work out how they may have been caused, since they may be caused by an error.

If you can explain why an anomalous result may be wrong, ignore it when working on your data. If you can't explain it then repeat it, if you can, but leave it in your results.

Apply your skills ▶▶ **B2, B6** ▶▶ **C3, C8, C10** ▶▶ **P4, P5**

anomalous results (outliers)

Figure A: Spotting anomalous results.

S20 MEANS AND RANGES

Repeated measurements usually vary. The **range** of the measurements is the difference between the highest and lowest values, often ignoring any **anomalous results (outliers)** that can be explained. The narrower the range of repeated measurements, the more sure you can be that they are correct.

The true value of the measurement will lie within the range. To **estimate** the true value we use the figures in the range to calculate an average called a **mean**:
- add up all your measurements
- divide by the number of measurements you took
- answer to the same number of **significant figures** as your original data

The more measurements used in the calculation, the better the estimate but the longer it takes.

How long do I take to zorb down this track?

Figure A: The mean time has been calculated in the example on the next page.

Test number	Time taken to zorb down the track (s)
1	24.0
2	24.6
3	24.5
4	82.7
5	24.5
6	24.4

Figure B: Calculating a mean.

There is one outlier in the data in the table – Test 4. This was caused by forgetting to stop the stopwatch. We ignore it, otherwise it will give us a poor estimate of the time taken.

Total = 122.6

Number of tests = 5

$$\text{Mean} = \frac{122.6}{5} = 24.4 \text{ s}$$

Apply your skills ▶▶ B5, B6 ▶▶ C1, C10 ▶▶ P3, P4, P7, P9

S21 VALIDITY

Something is **valid** if it does what it's meant to do.

An investigation is valid if the results let you answer the original question. A **fair test** is valid because you only measure the effects of the **independent variable**. You keep the **control variables** the same so they don't affect the **dependent variable**.

Results are valid if the measurements are what was meant to be measured and can be repeated. If control variables are not kept the same, the measurements are not valid because the dependent variable is affected by the independent variable *and* by other variables.

If the outcome of an investigation is unexpected, you need to check that the method is valid and the results are valid.

Apply your skills ▶▶ B4, B9 ▶▶ C3 ▶▶ P5

Figure A: A fencer intends to push the foil onto the darker grey part of the opponent's jacket. A hit is only valid if this happens.

You can be more sure of conclusions from an investigation if you have more data.

You should check measurements by repeating them. Measurements that are more or less the same (**precise**) when you repeat them are called **repeatable**. Repeatable measurements allow you to be more confident that you have good quality data.

Measurements that are very similar when repeated by others are **reproducible**. Reproducible measurements allow you to be even more confident of your data.

Good quality data:

- has repeatable (and preferably reproducible) measurements
- has many measurements over a **range** that is large enough to see a pattern
- does not have many **anomalous results**

Good quality data is said to be **reliable** and allows you to draw a firm conclusion.

Apply your skills ▶▶ **B2, B7** ▶▶ **C1** ▶▶ **P1, P2**

Figure A: Using the same make of bow, two archers both had repeatable shots. However, the two archers did not repeat each others' shots (the shots were not reproducible).

S23 TRIAL RUNS

When planning an investigation it is often difficult to know:

- the **range of measurements** to make (highest and lowest)
- what interval to have between the measurements
- how many measurements to make

In a **trial run** you carry out an investigation quickly, taking a few measurements over a large range. It lets you see a rough pattern, so you can work out the range and number of measurements you need to be sure of this pattern in the real investigation.

A trial run also means that you won't waste time taking unnecessary measurements in your investigation (e.g. by having too small an interval between measurements). It also lets you make sure that your method works, that you have the correct apparatus (including measuring devices of the right accuracy and resolution) and that your investigation is safe.

Apply your skills ▶▶ **B1, B4** ▶▶ **C8** ▶▶ **P3, P9**

Figure A: Some trial runs use scale models to test ideas before building a full-sized machine to test. This model aeroplane is being tested in a vertical wind tunnel.

S24 SAFETY: RISKS AND HAZARDS

You must plan safe investigations, which means thinking about the **hazards** of the apparatus, chemicals and methods that you want to use. A hazard is when something can cause a certain type of harm.

A **risk** is the chance of harm occurring from a hazard. You need to plan to reduce the risks from hazards like those in the table.

Hazard	Example of action to reduce risk
broken glass	reporting it to the teacher to get it cleaned up
chemicals	not breathing in dust
heating things	wearing eye protection
using electricity	switching off a power pack before altering a circuit
spills	mopping up immediately
living things	using disinfectants to kill micro-organisms

Apply your skills ⏭ **B8** ⏭ **C4, C8, C10** ⏭ **P3, P4, P7**

explosive   harmful to health   flammable

very toxic (poisonous)   harmful to breathing system   corrosive (attacks skin)

Figure A: Symbols are used to show the hazards of things, especially chemicals.

S25 PRIMARY AND SECONDARY DATA

Primary data (or **primary evidence**) `Name Check!` is data that you collect yourself, by doing investigations.
Secondary data (or **secondary evidence**) `Name Check!` is data collected by others.

Type of data	Advantages
Primary	You control the quality of the data
	You control what data is collected
	The data is up to date
	The data is relevant to your needs
Secondary	Quicker to obtain
	Easier to obtain
	Doesn't cost much to get it

Apply your skills ⏭ **B3, B5** ⏭ **C2** ⏭ **P5**

S26 SYMBOLS AND CONVENTIONS

A **symbol** is a way of representing something with a shape. A **convention** is a certain way of doing things. Scientists use conventions and symbols because they can:

* speed up writing things down
* make things look clearer
* be understood all over the world no matter what language is spoken.

Apply your skills ⏩ **B6** ⏩ **C2, C5, C8** ⏩ **P5, P9**

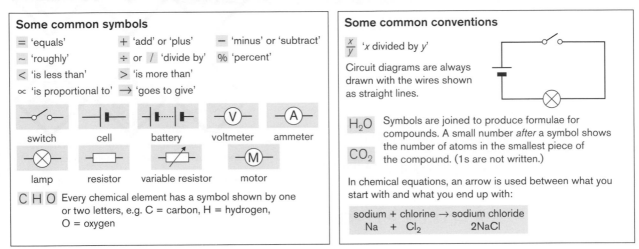

Some common symbols

= 'equals'	+ 'add' or 'plus'	− 'minus' or 'subtract'
∼ 'roughly'	÷ or / 'divide by'	% 'percent'
< 'is less than'	> 'is more than'	
∝ 'is proportional to'	→ 'goes to give'	

switch   cell   battery   voltmeter   ammeter

lamp   resistor   variable resistor   motor

C H O Every chemical element has a symbol shown by one or two letters, e.g. C = carbon, H = hydrogen, O = oxygen

Some common conventions

$\frac{x}{y}$ 'x divided by y'

Circuit diagrams are always drawn with the wires shown as straight lines.

H_2O Symbols are joined to produce formulae for compounds. A small number *after* a symbol shows the number of atoms in the smallest piece of the compound. (1s are not written.)

CO_2

In chemical equations, an arrow is used between what you start with and what you end up with:

sodium + chlorine → sodium chloride
  Na   + Cl_2 2NaCl

Figure A: Some common symbols and conventions used in science.

S27 FRACTIONS, PERCENTAGES, RATIOS AND DECIMALS

A **fraction** tells you how much of something there is. The 'thing' is divided into equal parts and the *total possible number* of parts goes on the bottom of the fraction. This is the **denominator**. The *actual number* of parts is put on the top. This is the **numerator**.

Scientific calculators can be used to add, subtract, multiply or divide fractions. Make sure you have a calculator that can do this and you know how to use it.

A **percentage** (%) is a fraction in which the denominator is 100. So 15% means '15 parts out of 100'. To show a fraction as a percentage, multiply it by 100. You should be able to do this with a calculator.

You might want to calculate a percentage of a number. To do this, you multiply the number by the percentage, as a fraction or decimal. For example to calculate 9% of 2000, multiply 2000 by 9/100, which is the same as 2000 × 0.09.

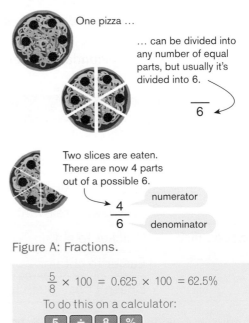

One pizza …

… can be divided into any number of equal parts, but usually it's divided into 6.

$$\frac{}{6}$$

Two slices are eaten. There are now 4 parts out of a possible 6.

$$\frac{4}{6}$$ numerator / denominator

Figure A: Fractions.

$\frac{5}{8} \times 100 = 0.625 \times 100 = 62.5\%$

To do this on a calculator:

5 ÷ 8 %

or   5 ÷ 8 × 1 0 0

Figure B: Converting fractions to percentages.

To find out how much larger (or smaller) one number is compared to another, you divide one number by the other and multiply by 100. So, for example, if we want to know what percentage 6 is of 12, we write '6 of 12' as '6 / 12'. Then, 6/12 = ½ or 0.5. As a percentage 0.5 × 100 = 50 %. 6 is 50% of 12.

A **ratio** is a way to compare two quantities. If Team A has 2 points and Team B has 3 points there is a '2 to 3 ratio', which is written as 2:3.

A number that is not a **whole number (integer)** **Name Check!** can be either a decimal or a fraction. A **decimal** is a line of digits. If there's no decimal point it's a **whole number** (there's an unwritten decimal point at the end).

Apply your skills ⏩ **B1, B2, B4** ⏩ **C1, C3, C8, C9** ⏩ **P3, P6, P7, P8, P9**

- To convert a fraction to a decimal, divide the numerator by the denominator.

$$\frac{3}{4} = 3 \div 4 = 0.75$$

- To convert a decimal to a fraction find out how many tenths, hundredths etc. there are after the decimal point and show these as a fraction.

2.4 is 2 and 4 tenths $= 2\frac{4}{10} = 2\frac{2}{5}$

8.35 is 8 and 35 hundredths

$$= 8\frac{35}{100} = 8\frac{7}{20}$$

Figure C: Converting decimals and fractions.

S28 PERCENTILES, DECILES AND QUARTILES

HIGHER A **percentile** is a value at which a certain percentage of some data is cut off. So the 16th percentile cuts off the first 16% of the values. In other words, 16% of the data have values that are equal to or below that value. If you are at the 16th percentile for height in your school, it would mean than 16% of students are your height or shorter.

A **decile** is the same idea but the data is divided into 10 equal parts (rather than 100). The 1st decile is the same as the 10th percentile.

A **quartile** is the same idea again but the data is divided into 4 parts. The **median** is the middle value of a whole data set, splitting a data set into 2 parts.

If *n* is the number of values in the data set, the median is the 0.5 × (*n* + 1)th value

The lower quartile is the middle value of the lower half of the data set, so the 0.25 × (*n* + 1)th value

The upper quartile is the middle value of the upper half of the data set, so the = 0.75 × (*n* + 1) th value

Apply your skills ⏩ **B10** ⏩ **C5** ⏩ **P8**

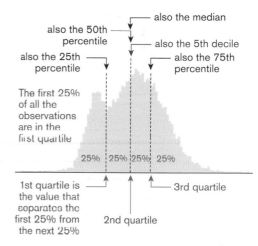

Figure A: Quartiles, deciles and percentiles.

S29 PROBABILITY

There are six sides on a die, with a different number on each side. The die is equally likely to land showing any one of the six numbers. So if you throw the die six times, you should get each number once. This doesn't always happen because throwing a die is a **random** process and so we talk about the chance or **probability** of a number being thrown. In the case of a die, the probability of throwing a four is 1 in 6.

A probability can be written as a fraction, a decimal or a percentage.

Most commonly, probabilities are written as decimals on a scale of 0–1 (where 1 means it's certain that something will happen). The probabilities of all the possible outcomes always add up to 1. So, it follows that if there is a 0.17 chance of throwing a certain number on a die, there is a $1 - 0.17 = 0.83$ chance of not throwing that number.

Apply your skills ▶▶ **B1, B8, B9** ▶▶ **C7** ▶▶ **P8**

There is a 1 in 6 chance of throwing a five. This can be written as a probability, which may be shown as a fraction, percentage or decimal of 1 or less: $\frac{1}{6}$ or 0.17 or 17%

Figure A: Ways of writing a probability.

S30 TABLES

Tables are used to record data but do not contain information about **control variables** or how variables were measured. There is a standard way of setting out a table, as shown in Figure A alongside.

If you design a table when planning an investigation it helps you think about:

✗ what **independent** and **dependent variables** to choose
✗ the range of measurements to use
✗ the intervals to have between measurements
✗ how to measure the dependent variable.

Tables are also used to present small sets of data because they allow you to put data in different orders. This helps you to look for patterns.

Apply your skills ▶▶ **B8, B10** ▶▶ **C2, C4, C9** ▶▶ **P2, P7**

independent variable   dependent variable

Time (mins)	Temperature of water (°C)
0	24.0
1	31.1
2	38.7
3	46.3
4	54.2
5	62.1

interval, range

Figure A: Temperature increase of 300 cm³ of water heated by burning 30 cm³ of oak wood.

Bar charts are usually used to present data in which the **independent variable** is **qualitative** (**categoric**) and the **dependent variable** (the one that you measure) is **quantitative**.

Generally, the independent variable is plotted on the horizontal axis (*x*-axis). The dependent variable is on the vertical axis (*y*-axis). It can be done the other way around but the bars always come out of which ever axis the independent variable is on.

Error bars show the range of measurements used to calculate average measurements. Shorter error bars show more precise measurements.

Always give your charts a title.

dependent variable
Write in its name and units.

Choose a scale so that the bars fill as much of the graph paper as possible. Number the scale and remember that the intervals must be equal.

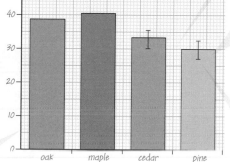

Temperature reached by 300 cm³ of water heated for 2 minutes by burning 30 cm³ of different types of wood.

Gaps are left between the bars to make it easier to read.

Bars are drawn:
• with a ruler
• with equal widths
• from each category up to the correct level.
This bar tells you that pine raised the temperature of the water by 30 °C.

Error bars are sometimes added and show the range of readings used to calculate an average. The range is often given as a percentage.

independent variable   Write in its name.

Figure A: A bar chart.

If you want to show how several things in different groups change, you can group the bars together.

Make the bars for the different things different colours or patterns.

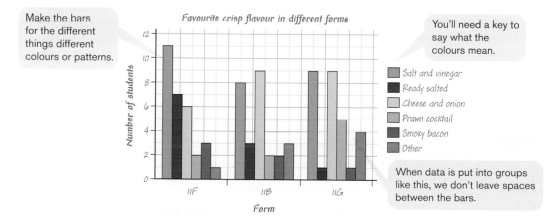

Favourite crisp flavour in different forms

You'll need a key to say what the colours mean.

■ Salt and vinegar
■ Ready salted
■ Cheese and onion
■ Prawn cocktail
■ Smoky bacon
■ Other

When data is put into groups like this, we don't leave spaces between the bars.

Apply your skills ▶▶ **B4** ▶▶ **C7**

Figure B: A bar chart with bars shown in groups.

HISTOGRAMS

Histograms are used when the:

* **independent variable** is **continuous data** that is put into groups
* **dependent variable** is related to the number of things (**frequency**).

The bars show how the continuous data has been put into groups.

Apply your skills ▶▶ **B9**

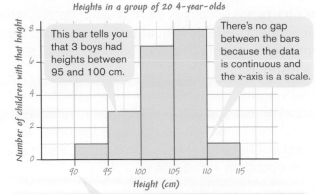

Heights in a group of 20 4-year-olds

This bar tells you that 3 boys had heights between 95 and 100 cm.

There's no gap between the bars because the data is continuous and the x-axis is a scale.

When grouping your data you need to decide where to put measurements that fall exactly on your boundaries. So a measurement of 95.1 would be counted in the second bar but you might decide to include 100.0 in the third bar. Just make sure you follow the same rule each time this happens.

Figure A: A histogram is often drawn with a scale on the x-axis.

S33 LINE GRAPHS

Line graphs are used to present data when both the **independent variable** and the **dependent variable** are in the form of **quantitative data**. They are used to show how one variable changes with another. The independent variable is usually time.

The independent variable is plotted on the horizontal axis (x-axis). The dependent variable is plotted on the vertical axis (y-axis).

If you need to plot more than one line on the same graph, it's a good idea to use ×s to plot one set of points and +s or circles to plot the other.

Always give your graphs a title.

Plot each point, in pencil, with a neat ×. Then connect the points with a straight line, using a ruler.

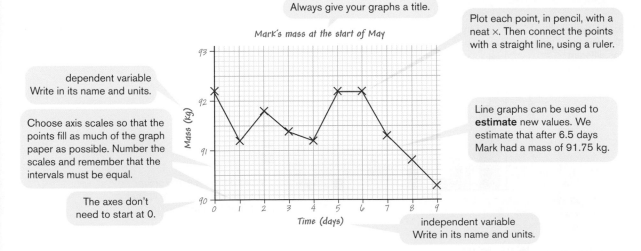

Mark's mass at the start of May

dependent variable
Write in its name and units.

Choose axis scales so that the points fill as much of the graph paper as possible. Number the scales and remember that the intervals must be equal.

The axes don't need to start at 0.

Line graphs can be used to **estimate** new values. We estimate that after 6.5 days Mark had a mass of 91.75 kg.

independent variable
Write in its name and units.

Apply your skills ▶▶ **B9** ▶▶ **C7** ▶▶ **P5**

Figure A: A line graph.

Scatter graphs (or **scattergrams** or **scatter plots**)
Name Check! are used when you want to find a
correlation between two variables. They are used when
both the variables are **continuous data**.

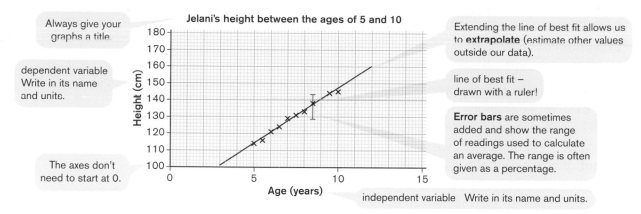

Always give your graphs a title.

dependent variable
Write in its name
and units.

The axes don't
need to start at 0.

Jelani's height between the ages of 5 and 10

Extending the line of best fit allows us
to **extrapolate** (estimate other values
outside our data).

line of best fit –
drawn with a ruler!

Error bars are sometimes
added and show the range
of readings used to calculate
an average. The range is often
given as a percentage.

independent variable   Write in its name and units.

Figure A: A line of best fit.

A **line of best fit** is often drawn through the points on a
scatter graph. The line goes through the middle of the
points, so that about half the points are on either side of
it. Note that the line of best fit does not necessarily have
to go through the origin (zero). You ignore any **anomalous
data** (**outliers**) when drawing a line of best fit.

For some data a **curve of best fit** is used. To draw a
curve of best fit, place your paper on the desk so that
the curve of points is shaped like an arch as you look at
it. Then put your elbow on the desk and practise moving
your hand in an arc, so that your pencil goes through the
points, but don't put the pencil on the paper. You may
need to experiment with the exact positioning of the
paper. When you've practised a few times, put the pencil
on the paper and draw a smooth curve.

For some data you will need a combination of lines of
best fit and curves of best fit.

Figure B: Drawing a curve of best fit.

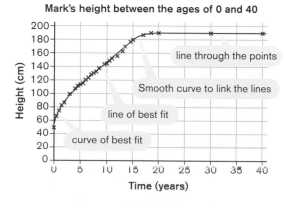

Mark's height between the ages of 0 and 40

line through the points

Smooth curve to link the lines

line of best fit

curve of best fit

Figure C: Lines and curves
of best fit can often be
used together.

Apply your skills ▶▶ **B5, B9** ▶▶ **C3, C9** ▶▶ **P2, P9**

Lines on graphs can be used to:
- estimate other values within your data
- estimate other values outside your data (**extrapolation**)
- calculate the **gradient** of a line (the resulting units will be the vertical axis units divided by the horizontal axis units)
- see if two variables are proportional

If two variables are **directly proportional**, when one changes the other changes in the same way by the same percentage. A straight line through the origin on a graph shows direct proportion and we write it as A ∝ B. The **constant of proportionality** is the amount we need to multiply an x-axis value to equal the y-axis value on the line. This constant often has the symbol 'm'. So, to calculate values for y on the line, we can use the formula: $y = mx$. The constant of proportionality is the gradient of the line.

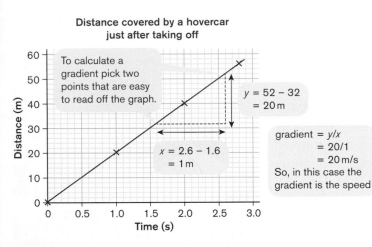

Distance covered by a hovercar just after taking off

To calculate a gradient pick two points that are easy to read off the graph.

$y = 52 - 32$
$= 20\,m$

$x = 2.6 - 1.6$
$= 1\,m$

gradient $= y/x$
$= 20/1$
$= 20\,m/s$
So, in this case the gradient is the speed

Figure A: The gradient of a line contains valuable information.

If the line does not go through the origin the formula becomes $y = mx + c$, where c is the value at which the line crosses the y-axis.

HIGHER If variables are inversely proportional A ∝ 1/B and so $y = m/x$. A graph of A against B showing inverse proportion will be a curve. For a straight line, plot A against 1/B.

Apply your skills ▶▶ **B9** ▶▶ **C7, C8, C9** ▶▶ **P6, P9**

S36 PIE CHARTS

Pie charts are used to compare the contributions made by different categories to a whole. A pie chart is a circle and so has 360°. These 360° are divided up into the same proportions as the different categories.

Favourite flavour of crisps	Number of students in class 11F
cheese & onion	6
other	1
prawn cocktail	2
ready salted	7
salt & vinegar	11
smoky bacon	3

Step 1: Add up the total number.
total is 30

Step 2: Divide 360° by the total number.
360/30 = 12 (so each student is represented by 12° of the circle)

Step 3: Multiply the number in each category by your answer to step 2.
e.g. 6 × 12 = 72

Include a title.

Neatly label your categories.

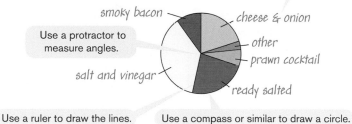

Favourite crisps in class 11F

smoky bacon — cheese & onion — other — prawn cocktail — salt and vinegar — ready salted

Use a protractor to measure angles.

Use a ruler to draw the lines.

Use a compass or similar to draw a circle.

Figure A: Drawing a pie chart.

Apply your skills ▶▶ **B1, B4**

S37 VENN DIAGRAMS

Venn diagrams are used to show associations between different groups of things. Each group is shown as a circle or oval. If two groups share items, the circles/ovals overlap.

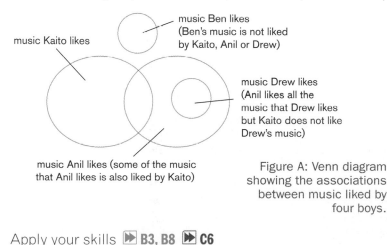

music Ben likes (Ben's music is not liked by Kaito, Anil or Drew)

music Kaito likes

music Drew likes (Anil likes all the music that Drew likes but Kaito does not like Drew's music)

music Anil likes (some of the music that Anil likes is also liked by Kaito)

Figure A: Venn diagram showing the associations between music liked by four boys.

Apply your skills ▶▶ **B3, B8** ▶▶ **C6**

The table shows when you need to use the different charts, graphs and diagrams.

Presentation type		Independent variable	Dependent variable	Used ...	Skill
Table		qualitative or quantitative	qualitative or quantitative	to record data and put it in order	S30
Bar chart		qualitative or quantitative, discrete	quantitative	to compare differences between groups	S31
Histogram		quantitative, continuous (grouped)	quantitative (usually a frequency)	to show how the number of times something occurs is distributed	S32
Line graph		quantitative, continuous (usually time)	quantitative	mainly to show how something changes with time	S33
Scatter graph		quantitative, continuous	quantitative	to find relationships between variables	S34
Pie chart		to compare the contributions of things to a whole			S36
Venn diagram		to show associations between different groups			S37
Flow chart		to show how one part of a process follows another			S1

Apply your skills ▶▶ B6, B7 ▶▶ C2, C3, C7, C10 ▶▶ P4, P6, P7, P8, P9, P10

S39 CONCLUSIONS

A **conclusion** is a decision that is made after considering all the evidence.

QWC A conclusion section in an investigation report must be organised to make it easy to follow. You could use this structure:

* state what you believe you have found out (your **opinion**)
* explain how your results support your opinion
* say whether your opinion agrees with your **prediction** or how they differ.

Your conclusion must also:

* be **valid**, which means that it must be drawn from the results. It must not say things that cannot be worked out from the results.
* use scientific words (like the ones in bold on these pages).

Apply your skills ▶▶ **B5, B6, B7, B10** ▶▶ **C3, C10** ▶▶ **P1, P5**

S40 MODELS

A **model** is anything that represents a thing or a process in a way that makes it easier for us to understand. Models usually simplify the real nature of something.

Models can be physical (you can touch them) or abstract (they are ways of thinking about things).

Investigations can be used to create new models and test existing models. Models can also be used to think up **hypotheses** and make **predictions**.

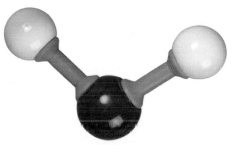

Figure A: This physical model represents the atoms in a molecule of water.

A chemical equation has an arrow:

hydrogen + oxygen → water

What you start with   the arrow means   What you end up with
'goes to give'

A mathematical formula usually has an equals sign:

$F = PA$ — This could be written $F = P \times A$ but the $\times$ is often just left out.

$F = 10 \times 3$

$= 30$ — If we know the values of P and A, we can calculate F.

Figure B: Equations are abstract models.

HIGHER F is the 'subject' of the formula but we can change this by rearranging. When you move something across the equals sign, it becomes opposite. So moving 'multiplied by A' across the equals sign becomes 'divided by A'. If you move $+x$ it becomes $-x$.

$\dfrac{F}{A} = P$ — This is the same as $P = \dfrac{F}{A}$
P is now the subject.

Apply your skills ▶▶ **B2, B6** ▶▶ **C1, C3, C7, C9** ▶▶ **P3, P8, P10**

S41 ARGUMENTS

QWC An **argument** is a way of telling people what you think and why you think it. A good argument will have the following structure:

* a statement of what you think (your **opinion**)
* an explanation of why you think this, with supporting evidence
* a **counterargument** – an explanation of why others may not agree with you
* a response – explaining why the counterargument is wrong
* a summary – stating your opinion again

QWC The **conclusion** section in an investigation report may contain an argument. Arguments in articles may use persuasive language as well as evidence, including: repeating pieces of evidence, exaggerating, using emotional language to play on feelings, and asking questions of the reader.

Apply your skills ▶▶ **B5, B8** ▶▶ **C4** ▶▶ **P3, P4, P7**

Figure A: An argument.

S42 EVALUATING

An **evaluation** is a look at how well something does its job. When you evaluate your investigations, or those of others, ask yourself questions about the method, results and conclusions:

* Is the investigation **valid**? (Do the results let you answer the question?)
* Are the measurements valid? (Do they measure what they were supposed to?)
* How **precise** are the results? (Were there lots of **anomalous results**?)
* Why did any anomalous results appear?
* Were the results **accurate** enough to draw a conclusion?
* How **repeatable** or **reproducible** are the results?
* Are the results and/or conclusions unbiased? (Or is there **bias** trying to persuade you that the results show something that they don't really show?)
* Is the **conclusion** valid? (Has it been drawn from only the results?)
* Have any false **assumptions** been made? (Assumptions are things that everyone accepts as true so you don't test them, e.g. the Earth is like a ball.)

You should try to **justify** your answers.

Apply your skills ▶▶ **B5, B9** ▶▶ **C3, C10** ▶▶ **P7, P9**

QWC Scientists tell others about their ideas by giving talks at conferences and writing **papers**. A paper has the same form as an investigation report:

* abstract – an overview
* introduction – discusses other research in this area
* methods – what was done and how it was done
* results
* conclusion – what the results show and why
* references – all the papers, websites etc. used to write the paper

A paper is sent to a **journal** (a magazine for scientific papers).

The editors of journals send papers that look good to experts in the same subject as the paper. These scientists **evaluate** the investigations and check that the **conclusions** can be drawn from the results. They then say whether the paper should be published or if changes are needed. This is called **peer review**.

A scientist may not agree with the conclusions in a paper since scientists often develop different ideas to explain the same data. Only further experiments can settle the matter but the paper can still be published.

A reviewing scientist checks that the results are not **biased** (shifted in a certain direction). Poor investigation design or poor measuring can cause bias. However, sometimes scientists cause bias on purpose to:

* please people who employ them
* become famous
* make money

A theory is not discarded until a new theory that fully explains all the observations has been developed. This involves many investigations and papers – not just one (which may be biased or contain **anomalous results**). Scientists tend not to believe evidence that is not **repeatable** or **reproducible**. However, evidence may be given more importance if it's from a famous or well-respected scientist.

Apply your skills ▶▶ **B3, B7, B9** ▶▶ **C1, C2, C6, C9** ▶▶ **P1, P6, P10**

Figure A: The journal *Science* comes out every week.

scientist sends paper to journal

checked by editor and sent to other scientists for comments

based on feedback from the scientists, the editor decides whether to publish

Figure B: The peer review process.

S44 BENEFITS, DRAWBACKS AND RISKS

A **benefit** is a good thing that comes from something. The opposite of a benefit is a **drawback**. A **risk** is how likely it is that a drawback will cause harm.

Scientific research allows the development of new technologies and ways of doing things. These all have benefits, drawbacks and risks.

Apply your skills ▶ **B8, B9** ▶ **C3, C5, C8** ▶ **P1, P3, P10**

Benefits	Drawbacks	Risks
• discovery of what the Moon is like • study the effects of microgravity on humans • invention of new materials and technologies (e.g. memory foam)	• expense • danger • harm to the environment	• astronauts quite likely to die • animals likely to be killed by launch • ozone layer may be damaged by fuels

Figure A: A few of the benefits, drawbacks and risks of sending people to the Moon.

S45 RISKS AND DECISIONS

Everything we do carries a **risk** of harm. The size of a risk is sometimes measured by taking a large **sample** and counting the number of times something causes harm.

New technologies can create new **hazards** or **drawbacks** with risks of harm. For example, older women may use hormone replacement therapy (HRT), which increases the risk of breast cancer. When people make decisions (e.g. taking HRT) they consider the benefits, the level of risk and the consequences if the worst happens.

Risk of breast cancer ...	per 10 000	percentage
... without HRT	10 in 10 000	0.1%
... with HRT	13 in 10 000	0.13%

When people make decisions for themselves, they accept a certain level of risk. They are also more likely to decide to do things if the possible harm won't last very long (e.g. risk of a broken arm) compared to when the possible harm is long-lasting.

Public bodies (e.g. councils) compare the benefits and drawbacks of a change, and assess the levels of risks they think people should accept (e.g. the risk to health of building an incinerator). However, people are less likely to accept levels of risk when they have not been given a choice.

People often think that the level of risk is higher than it actually is, particularly when the risk is from things that are unfamiliar, invisible, or may cause long-term harm.

Apply your skills ▶ **B2, B8** ▶ **C7** ▶ **P7, P8**

To decide whether to use a new scientific development, people must consider all the things that might happen, both good and bad, including:

- the financial costs
- the effect on the environment
- the effect on people (both individuals and different groups)
- ethics (see below)

QWC Decisions are usually explained in a report. The report is divided into sections. There is a section for each of the points on the list above. Each section will:

- consider if the benefits are greater than the drawbacks
- consider if any risks can be reduced
- be based on **valid**, **repeatable** and **reproducible** evidence (not on attitudes, myths or rumours)

If a decision is likely to be unpopular, in a poor report evidence against the decision might be hidden or the importance of favourable evidence may be over-stated.

Decisions can take time, with long reports being written. Sometimes a **public enquiry** is held, in which everyone can give an opinion. In the end, not everybody will agree with a decision, especially those at risk from harm or those who don't benefit.

Some new technologies cause ethical and moral problems. **Morals** involve actions that a person thinks is right or wrong. **Ethics** involve actions that a group of people agree are right or wrong (e.g. stealing is wrong). People may disagree over ethical issues (e.g. experiments on human embryos). Often an ethical decision is based on whatever leads to the best outcome for the greatest number of people.

Ethics and risks mean that many areas of science are governed by rules. These are decided upon by experts and are often made into laws.

Apply your skills ▶▶ **B4, B6, B7, B8** ▶▶ **C4, C8** ▶▶ **P1, P4, P5**

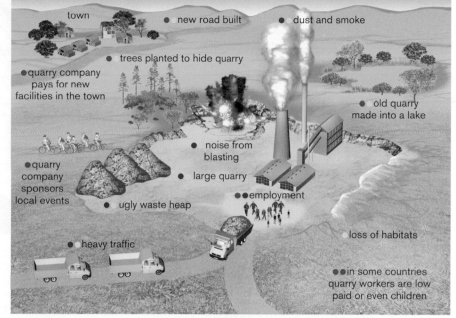

town • new road built • dust and smoke

• trees planted to hide quarry

• quarry company pays for new facilities in the town

• old quarry made into a lake

• noise from blasting

• quarry company sponsors local events

• large quarry

•• employment

• ugly waste heap

loss of habitats

• heavy traffic

•• in some countries quarry workers are low paid or even children

Figure A: Some factors to consider when deciding whether to build a new quarry. Some factors are more important than others.

Figure B: Scientists present a decision at a press conference.

S47 SCIENCE IN THE MEDIA

QWC Science is reported and commented on by many individuals and organisations in different **media** (e.g. TV, newspapers, internet). A good article will:

- be clear in its meaning, including good grammar and spelling
- contain up-to-date information
- provide evidence for any claims that are made
- contain good quality (reliable) data
- present both sides of a debate, although it may try to persuade you to believe one side (e.g. by using an **argument**, a lot of repetition or emotional language)
- reveal all of the sources of information used to write the article

You should evaluate scientific articles using these points.

Apply your skills ▶▶ **B7, B10** ▶▶ **C2, C7** ▶▶ **P8**

Figure A: Some articles cause controversy. Simon Singh said that the British Chiropractic Association (BCA) should not promote treatments that had little evidence of being effective. The BCA took him to court but dropped the case.

S48 ANALYSING AND SYNTHESISING

Scientists need to understand other scientists' ideas and form their own **opinions**. They then tell others about their opinions by presenting **arguments** in journal **papers** or in TV and radio broadcasts or in letters and articles in magazines and newspapers.

When you read, watch or listen to something that contains scientific information, you should analyse the information:

- What subject is being discussed?
- How has the writer or speaker organised the information?
- What are the main points and what evidence supports these points?
- What conclusion is drawn?

QWC If you take notes using the same structure for each article you will be able to make connections (e.g. spotting how the same evidence has been used differently, spotting points on which different authors agree or disagree). This will help you form your own opinions, which you can then write about.

Apply your skills ▶▶ **B4** ▶▶ **C7** ▶▶ **P7, P8**

When you analyse scientific information you should make notes. Some people like to take notes using tables, others prefer using headings and subheadings and others like to use concept maps. Your notes do not need to be seen by anyone else, but you should be able to read them back again and understand what they mean.

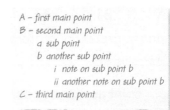
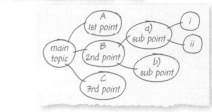

A – first main point
B – second main point
  a sub point
  b another sub point
    i note on sub point b
    ii another note on sub point b
C – third main point

When examining a text:

* read it through quickly first, concentrating on understanding it
* read it through slowly, writing down unfamiliar words (which you may need to look up)
* write down the main ideas and points (but use short, summary-style sentences and in your own words; it's pointless just copying out chunks of a text)
* add arrows and symbols to link ideas together and highlight important points

Figure A: There are many different ways of structuring your notes.

QWC When it comes to planning your own writing, think about PAF (Figure B).

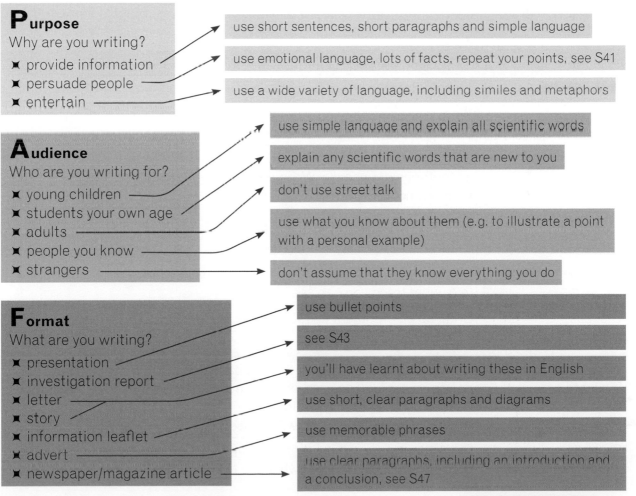

Purpose
Why are you writing?
* provide information
* persuade people
* entertain

use short sentences, short paragraphs and simple language

use emotional language, lots of facts, repeat your points, see S41

use a wide variety of language, including similes and metaphors

Audience
Who are you writing for?
* young children
* students your own age
* adults
* people you know
* strangers

use simple language and explain all scientific words

explain any scientific words that are new to you

don't use street talk

use what you know about them (e.g. to illustrate a point with a personal example)

don't assume that they know everything you do

Format
What are you writing?
* presentation
* investigation report
* letter
* story
* information leaflet
* advert
* newspaper/magazine article

use bullet points

see S43

you'll have learnt about writing these in English

use short, clear paragraphs and diagrams

use memorable phrases

use clear paragraphs, including an introduction and a conclusion, see S47

Figure B: Think PAF when planning how to write something.

Continued overleaf →

QWC Before you actually start writing, it's a good idea to sketch out how you are going to organise your information. If you are writing an article, you will need to use paragraphs to group your information. You could use a structure like this:

- main idea (introduction)
  - first main point as a paragraph with details and evidence
  - second main point as a paragraph with details and evidence
  - etc.
- conclusion

QWC Always remember to check your punctuation, spelling and grammar too!

Apply your skills ▶▶ **B1–B5, B9, B10** ▶▶ **C1, C3, C5–C8, C10** ▶▶ **P1, P5–P9**

S50 COMMAND WORDS

QWC Words that tell you how to answer a question are called command words. It's important that you know what they all mean. The table will help you.

Command	Notes
Name Check! Assess	See 'Evaluate' below.
Calculate	Work out an answer using numbers. Always show your working. Always put in the units.
Compare	Describe the differences/similarities between things or their advantages/drawbacks. Write down something about all the things and then say how they are similar/different.
Complete	Fill in answers in a space or finish writing a sentence.
Define	State briefly what something means.
Describe	Recall facts in an accurate way or say what a diagram or graph shows (e.g. what trend you can see).
Discuss	Build up an argument about an issue.
Estimate	Make a rough calculation.
Name Check! Evaluate	Say how good or poor something is based on looking at a series of points (criteria). If you are asked to evaluate more than one thing then you need to compare the things (see 'Compare' above) and then state which of the things is best, with reasons why you think that.
Explain	State the reasons why something happens. You must explain the links between your reasons and what you are explaining – don't just write down a list of reasons.

Command	Notes
Name Check! Give	See 'Write down' below.
Identify	Look at some data or text and pick out a certain part.
Illustrate	Give examples in an explanation or description. A good way to do this is to explain/describe something and then use the words 'For example' to introduce an example.
Justify	Evaluate (see 'Evaluate' above) something that provides evidence for your choice of which is best.
List	Write down key points in a brief way.
Name Check! Name	See 'Write down' below.
Outline	State the main points of an argument or of how something happens. This can be done a list of bullet points.
Name Check! State	See 'Write down' below.
Suggest	Use your scientific knowledge to work out what is happening in an unfamiliar situation.
Summarise	See 'Outline' above.
Use the information	Use the information given to answer the question. You won't get any marks unless you use the information given.
Name Check! Write down	State a fact or give an example. If a question asks for two examples (or has two marks) only write down two. Otherwise, you risk writing something that is incorrect and losing marks.

Apply your skills ➤➤ **B1–B10** ➤➤ **C1–C10** ➤➤ **P1–P10**

Answers

There are answers to all the questions in this section. There are many different ways in which questions are asked, so have a look at S50 if some of the command words (the words at the start of a question telling you what to do) are a bit confusing.

Some of the answers have additional notes in *italics* next to them. These notes make general comments about a question and describe some common errors made in answering questions of a particular type.

🏠 Some answers have this icon. This means that there is a better way of answering the question, which you might have missed. In an exam, questions are given a number of marks. Sometimes a question might just have one mark and the basic answer will get you that mark. However, that same question may be worth two marks, in which case you'd need the 'better answer'. It's always good practice to write the best answers that you can!

QWC Some questions are QWC questions, which stands for 'Quality of Written Communication'. Most of these are the last question on each page, which are long-answer questions. In exams, questions like this are worth six marks and require a well-structured answer, in good English. To get all the marks, both the science and the English need to be good.

The table shows the key QWC skills:

| legibility of text; accuracy of spelling, punctuation and grammar; clarity of meaning |
| selection of a form and style of writing appropriate to purpose and to complexity of subject matter |
| organisation of information clearly and coherently; use of specialist vocabulary where appropriate |

In a six-mark, long-answer question you'll get **1–2 marks** if you:
- ✘ write down basic scientific information
- ✘ show a simple understanding of the science
- ✘ don't use many scientific words (or show a lack of understanding of their meaning)
- ✘ don't organise your answer
- ✘ don't include much detail
- ✘ use poor spelling, grammar and punctuation.

You'll get **3–4 marks** if you:
- ✘ write down accurate scientific information
- ✘ show a clear understanding of the science
- ✘ use some scientific words, some of which are not used properly
- ✘ try to organise your answer
- ✘ include some detail
- ✘ use reasonably accurate spelling, grammar and punctuation.

You'll get **5–6 marks** if you:
- ✘ write down scientific information that is always accurate and relevant
- ✘ show a detailed understanding of the science, which you demonstrate by giving evidence and examples
- ✘ use a wide range of relevant scientific words, which are all used properly
- ✘ organise your answer so that it forms a logical series of points
- ✘ include some detail
- ✘ use very accurate spelling, grammar and punctuation.

In the answer section for these questions, there is a list of points that you could have included in your answer. The points marked ★ are those that would be found in a 1–2 mark answer. The points marked ★★ are those that would be found in a 3–4 mark answer. The points marked ★★★ are those that would be found in a 5–6 mark answer.

On the following pages, three of the long-answer questions have been answered and comments have been made on the different answers. Have a look at these to help you write better longer answers.

6 Some blood cells are put in pure water. Explain what will happen.
▶▶ QWC S3, S49, S50

★ **Low level answer**

There are lots of misspellings in this answer. Learn the spellings of scientific words. You will lose marks in this sort of question for poor spelling.

Things can move into the sell and make changed the shape this is because water molickules can move. The sells get all big and fat.

This is poor grammar. It should read 'and change the shape'. You will lose marks in this sort of question for poor grammar.

This is poor punctuation. Sentences should end with a full stop and start with a capital letter, otherwise it is very difficult to read. This should read '… the shape. This is because …'.

This answer is not good. The spelling, punctuation and grammar are poor. The way in which it is written is not very logical either. Answers need to be written in a way that lets the reader follow a process in logical steps. It would make much more sense if it were written like this:

Things can move into cells and change their shape, making them big and fat. This is due to the movement of water molecules.

Two scientific points are made, however, and these would gain a mark or two.

★★ **Medium level answer**

This is a common spelling mistake. Learn the spellings of scientific words. You will lose marks in this sort of question for poor spelling. However, there is only one spelling mistake in this answer, which is good.

A sell can change it's shape when substances move into or out of it. This is called osmosis. If a blood sell is put in pure water, water molecule's move into it making it swell up.

This is poor grammar. The first line should read 'its shape'. When you are saying 'it is' then you can turn that into 'it's'. However, if you are saying that something belongs to 'it' then there is no apostrophe. This is a very common grammatical error. In the last sentence there is an apostrophe in molecules. This is also incorrect but is quite a common error. Plural nouns do not have apostrophes.

The punctuation in this answer is good.

There are a few scientific points that are made and presented in a fairly logical order and marks will be awarded for this. However, the question asks you to 'explain' how the process happens and this has not been done.

This is not correct. The moving of substances into and out of a cell is not osmosis. This term is only used to describe water moving through a selectively permeable membrane. Also, the position of that sentence is not great because it's not clear whether the student means that the process of substances moving is called osmosis or whether when a cell changes its shape it's called osmosis.

★★★ High level answer

This is excellent and makes good use of scientific words like 'membrane' and 'selectively permeable'.

There is a very clear explanation of osmosis, which is what the question asked for.

> The membrane of the blood cell is selectively permeable, which means that only water molecules can pass through it. If there are more water molecules on one side of the membrane than the other, there will be more water molecules that move through the membrane to the side where there are less of them (a process called osmosis). Fewer water molecules will move in the opposite direction. When a blood cell is put in pure water, there are more water molecules outside the cell and so there will be an overall movement of water molecules into the cell by osmosis. This will make the cell swell up.

The spelling, grammar and punctuation are all excellent.

This answer has a very good structure, giving a clear explanation of the process of osmosis before going back to the example in the question to show how the process applies to that example. This answer would get full marks.

C6 EARTH MOVING – WORKED EXAMPLE

6 Write a short article about how the theory of 'plate tectonics' developed.
▶▶ QWC S49, S50

★ Low level answer

This is wrong and is not spelt correctly. You will lose marks in this sort of question for poor spelling. Wegener thought of the theory of continental drift. The theory of plate tectonics was developed later, based on Wegener's ideas.

> Some scientists said wot Alfred Wegener said that wont be true becus you cannot measure the moving of continents. Alfred Wegener said that africa and south america fitted together like a jigsaw and so he thought of the theory of plate techtonics. This said that the continents were moving. Now we know that he was rite

This is poor grammar and spelling. It should read '... said that what Alfred Wegener said was not true ...'. You will lose marks in this sort of question for poor grammar.

This is poor punctuation. All proper nouns need to start with capital letters.

This is poor spelling. It should read 'right'. You will lose marks in this sort of question for poor spelling.

This answer is not good. The spelling, punctuation and grammar are poor. The way in which it is written is not very logical either. Answers need to be written in a way that lets the reader follow a process in logical steps. It would make much more sense if it were written like this:

> Alfred Wegener said that Africa and South America fitted together like a jigsaw and so he thought of the theory of continental drift, in which he said that the continents were moving. Some scientists said that what Alfred Wegener said was not true because you cannot measure the moving of continents. However, now we know that he was right.

Some scientific points are made, however, and these would gain a couple of marks.

★★ Medium level answer

This isn't quite right. The theory of plate tectonics has developed out of the Wegener's idea of continental drift.

These are spelling mistakes. It doesn't look good if you get the name wrong of scientist that you've just read about.

> Alfred Wagener came up with the hypothysis of continental drift in 1912. Today this idea has become plate tectonics.
>
> Wagener made observations that supported his idea. This included the fact that South America and Africa appear to fit together, a bit like a giant jigsaw.
>
> Many scientists disagreed with Wagener because he could neither explain how continents moved across a solid sea floor nor show that they were actually moving. In addition, he was not a geologist, he was German (people were suspicious of Germans in the time leading up to World War I) and other theories had simpler explanations for the observations (e.g. a land bridge had connected South America and Africa).

This whole paragraph has just been copied out of the page. You need to write articles in your own words. Copying chunks of other people's work is called plagiarism. You won't get marks for doing this and in this case there is a lot of information here that is of no relevance to the how the theory of plate tectonics was developed.

The grammar and punctuation are fine. The structure of the answer is fair. It starts with an opening paragraph that contains an overview and then it has a paragraph outlining Wegener's reasoning, followed by a paragraph on objections to Wegener. However, there is no attempt to explain how these objections were overcome or to say exactly what plate tectonics is. It's only half finished. Also, only one of Wegener's observations has been included.

★★★ High level answer

This is excellent and includes all of Wegener's observations.

There is a very clear and only contains details of the problems with Wegener's idea rather than details about the man himself, which are not relevant. The question asks for details about how plate tectonics developed.

> Alfred Wegener came up with the hypothesis of continental drift in 1912. Today this idea forms the basis of the theory of plate tectonics.
>
> Wegener made observations that made him think that the continents were moving. This included the fact that South America and Africa appear to fit together, a bit like a giant jigsaw. Also, the fossils and rocks found on these continents were the same.
>
> However, Wegener could not explain how the continents moved and nor could he show that they were moving.
>
> It wasn't until the 1950s that scientists discovered that the Earth's surface was cracked into huge plates. At this time, scientists also had measuring devices with greater sensitivity and these could show that these plates moved.
>
> Wegener's hypothesis of continental drift was changed by these discoveries and turned into the modern theory of plate tectonics.

The spelling, grammar and punctuation are all excellent. This answer has a very good structure: there is an overview paragraph, then a paragraph about how Wegener got his ideas, then a paragraph about the problems he faced, then a paragraph about how those problems were solved. The article ends with a clear summary.

3 Discuss the use of PET scans. Think about the benefits, drawbacks and risks.
▶▶ QWC **S24, S27, S41, S44, S50**

★ **Low level answer**

This is poor grammar.

Stomach is not spelt like this.

This not spelt correctly. PET is an abbreviation (for Positron Emission Tomography but you don't need to know that) and so is spelt with capital letters. It doesn't look good if you misspell words that are in the question.

This is poor punctuation. Lists need to have commas to separate out the different items. Also this sentence is just a space filler. Putting in a list of different cancers does not answer the question.

This word needs to be 'their' and not 'there'.

> Pet scans are good because they find cancer, which can kill people. They save a lot of lives because they finding lots of different sorts of cancer like stomack cancer lung cancer kidney cancer and brain cancer. This means that people with cancer can get treated because they will know that they have cancer. This save there lives. All hospitals should have a pet scanner.

This answer is not good. It contains many spelling, punctuation and grammatical mistakes and it does not answer the question. It may score one mark (for stating that the student is in favour of something and giving a reason why).

When you are asked to discuss something, you need to build up an argument (as shown in S41). There is no argument built here.

★★ **Medium level answer**

These are a spelling mistakes. Make sure you check your spelling, punctuation and grammar in your answers to longer questions, otherwise you will not get as many marks as you could.

These are good reasons against using PET scanners.

> PET scans can detect some cancers that other methods cannot detect. They are also quick and so paysents can get their results quickly and start their treatment quickly.
> However, PET scanners are very expensive and radioactive supstances are used, which can be dangerous.
> So overall I think that PET scanners are good things to have in hospitals.

This answer communicates what the student thinks. However, an argument has not been developed, the student has simply stated some reasons why PET scanners are a good thing and some reasons why they are not. An argument needs to have some reasons behind these statements.

★★★ High level answer

This is a clear opinion. Remember that an opinion is not necessarily right or wrong.

This is a good structure, with three clear paragraphs setting out and *explaining* the reasons why the student holds that opinion. The third paragraph also makes good use of emotive language to persuade the reader that they are right.

This is a clear counterargument, followed by a response saying why the student doesn't agree with the counterargument.

This is a very clear argument, with good spelling, grammar and punctuation.

I do not think that PET scans should be used in the UK.

PET scanners are very expensive, which uses up a great deal of money that would be better spent on treating more people.

Not every hospital can have a PET scanner because they need to be near a place where the radioactive tracers are made. This means that people may have to travel a long way to get a PET scan. It would be better to have cheaper alternatives in more hospitals.

Dangerous radioactivity is used, which can itself cause cancer. Although the risk of getting cancer from a PET scan is small it's large enough to mean that children and pregnant women aren't given PET scans. So why should other people be subjected to these scans?

Some people will say that PET scans allow smaller cancers to be found. However, there are plenty of other ways of detecting cancer and we should invest the money saved from PET scans into making these better.

The dangers and expense involved with PET scans means that we should stop using them.

1 An estimate is a rough calculation. *This is a straightforward question.*

2 a $5 \times 4 = 20 \, \text{km}^2$. *Don't forget the units. If there were marks for this question, it would be out of 2 – one for the correct calculation and one for the units.*

b 140/20 = 7. The whole area is 7 times bigger than the sample area. So, there are about 7×51 white rhinos in the whole area = 353.
🔺 A better answer would be to round this down to two significant figures, which is 350. The answer is an estimate and the two area measurements are given to two significant figures. *As a rule, give your answers to the same number of significant figures as most of the numbers in the question are given.*

3 14 500 : 250 = 58:1 *You need to cancel the ratio down, as you would a fraction, in order to get it into its simplest form.*

4 5/20 = ¼ or 0.25 or 25%. *You have three choices of how you express your answer!*

5 Proportions of the different species of rhinoceros

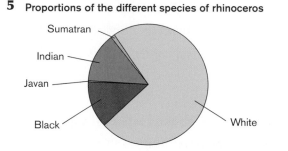

You've been asked to draw a pie chart for this data because you are showing the different proportions that contribute to a whole.

The angles you need are calculated like this:

Rhino	Sumatran	White	Black	Javan	Indian	Total
number	250	14500	2500	60	2650	19960
angle calculation 360/19910 = 0.018	250 × 0.018	14500 × 0.018	2500 × 0.018	60 × 0.018	2650 × 0.018	
angle	5°	261°	45°	1°	48°	360°

Make sure you have:
- *The correct angles*
- *A title*
- *All the categories neatly labelled*
- *Used a ruler to draw the lines*
- *Used a compass or similar to draw the circle*

6 The equipment needs to be checked to make sure it works. Specifically, the automatic cameras need to be tried with real animals (or maybe Sumatran rhinos in captivity) to make sure that they do take photos when an animal walks past.

7 **QWC** *This is a QWC question – see page 76. You need to check your spelling, grammar and punctuation and try to include scientific words, such as 'sample' and 'estimate'.*

You should try to include some of the points in the list below. You don't need to make all the points but you should aim to make points with the more stars. If you make 3 or 4 good scientific points in a question like this, and write your answer in good English, you will get 6 marks in an exam. Check your answer with the points below, the grade booster box on page 10 and the general points about QWC answers on page 76.

★ you would need to count the numbers of white rhinos in different years
★ if the numbers are increasing or staying about the same, conservation efforts are working
★ you count the number of rhinos in a sample area of known size
★ this allows you to calculate an estimate of the number of rhinos
★ you multiply the number of rhinos counted by how many times bigger the whole area is compared with the sample area
★★ you don't need an exact number to know if generally the number of rhinos is increasing or decreasing
★★ there are too many white rhinos to count each one

★★★ counting rhinos individually would take too long/be too expensive

★★★ it would be very hard to get an exact number because rhinos will be being born and dying whilst the count is going on

To get the most marks for a question like this, you need to justify your answer. This means explaining why the way in which something is done is the best way of doing it.

B2 SALTY SNACKS

1 $1/100\,000 \times 100 = 0.001\ \%$

2 Qualitative – there are no numbers.

3 A membrane that allows only some substances (e.g. water) to pass through it. *This question requires you to have understood how this sort of membrane works (from the text) and to have examined Figure C in enough detail to find out what a membrane like this is called.*

4 To help them to understand how something works. (They can also be used to make predictions but you won't have got that from this page.) *This is a straightforward question to make sure you understand what a model is.*

5 a There are two points here. If this were a 1 mark question you would only need one point, if it were a 2 mark question you would need both points:

- because using a single cell may give an anomalous result/outlier
- the more measurements you make, the more sure you can be of what you are observing.

b Using pure water. *A control is usually a repeat of the experiment in which the independent (input) variable is not applied.*

c Two from: the type of salt, the type of cell, the temperature, the apparatus used, the volume of salt solution, the number of cells.

6 **QWC** *There are some examples of answers to this question, and comments on those answers, on pages 77–78. This is a QWC question – see page 76. You need to check your spelling, grammar and punctuation and try to include scientific words, such as 'dilute', 'concentrated', 'osmosis', 'membrane' and 'molecule'.*

If a question asks you to explain something then take great care that you <u>explain how</u> something is happening, and you don't just <u>describe what</u> happens. You could answer this question more clearly by using a model. You could draw a version of Figure C as part of your answer.

You should try to include some of the points in the list below. You don't need to make all the points but you should aim to make points with the more stars. If you make 3 or 4 good scientific points in a question like this, and write your answer in good English, you will get 6 marks in an exam. Check your answer with the points below, the grade booster box on page 11 and the general points about QWC answers on page 76.

★ the cells will change shape

★ substances can move into and out of the cell

★★ osmosis occurs

★★ water moves into the cells

★★ the cells swell up/become rounder

★★★ water molecules move from a place where there are more of them (more dilute solution) to a place where there are less of them (more concentrated solution)

★★★ other molecules of dissolved substances cannot go through the membrane, so only the water can move

★★★ the membrane is selectively permeable

★★★ more water molecules move into the cell than out of the cell (another way of saying this is that there is 'a net movement' of water molecules into the cells)

B3 DAR-WINS!

1 A theory is a scientific idea that is supported by a lot of evidence. A hypothesis is a scientific idea that has little or no evidence to support it (but no evidence against it).

2 Reading Malthus' essay. *Remember to read the question carefully. This question is about how evolution works and not about what evolution is (gradual changes in organisms).*

3

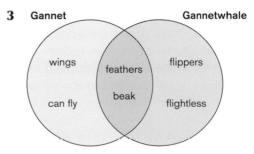

Gannet — wings, can fly; feathers, beak; Gannetwhale — flippers, flightless

4 a Secondary

b Two of: you can't control the quality of the data, the scientists who find different fossils may interpret them in different ways, the scientists who find different fossils may dig them up using different techniques, the drawings/photographs of the fossils may not be very good, the drawings/photographs of the fossils may not show the features you are interested in.

5 **HIGHER** 35 million years ago is $35\,000\,000 = 3.5 \times 10^7$ years ago

6 It may cause bias. The fossil may be the only one that shows a certain feature whereas all the other members of this species did not have that feature at the time.

7 **QWC** *This is a QWC question – see page 76. You need to check your spelling, grammar and punctuation and try to include scientific words, such as 'evolution', 'theory', 'evidence', and 'species'.*

You need to really look at all the information that you've been given on the page. When writing a long answer like this, you need to give relevant examples as part of your explanation.

You should try to include some of the points in the list below. You don't need to make all the points but you should aim to make points with the more stars. If you make 3 or 4 good scientific points in a question like this, and write your answer in good English, you will get 6 marks in an exam. Check your answer with the points below, the grade booster box on page 12 and the general points about QWC answers on page 76.

★ scientists have collected a lot of evidence for this idea
★ the evidence fits/supports the theory
★ scientists are still discovering new evidence that supports the theory
★★ similar species of animals with slight differences are found in environments with slight differences
★★★ if ground becomes drier and harder, animals with smaller feet can move faster across it. Over time, the animals that could move faster to escape predators survived and passed this characteristic on to their offspring. Horse fossils show a gradual change from splayed toes (to provide support on wet ground) to small hooves.
★★★ if vegetation changes from softer leaves to harder grasses, animals with larger and harder teeth can feed better. Over time, the animals

that could better chew grass survived and passed this characteristic on to their offspring. Horse fossil teeth show a gradual increase in size and hardness.
★★★ if grasslands replace forests, taller animals get a better view of predators. Over time, the animals that could better see predators survived and passed this characteristic on to their offspring. Horse fossils show a gradual increase in size.

B4 FISHY TREATMENTS

1 **QWC** A reduction in the symptoms of psoriasis depends on fish/*Garra rufa* eating dead skin. *Or you could have written 'Garra rufa can help psoriasis'. You don't have to use 'depends on' but it often helps you to write a hypothesis correctly.*

2 People swimming in the Kangal hot spring in Turkey.

3 • dependent (output) variable: amount of psoriasis or reduction in pain/itching/skin scaliness
• independent (input) variable: skin-eating fish
• control variables: type of fish, length of treatment. *You'll notice that there are some other control variables that don't seem to have been controlled, such as the number of fish and age of the patients. Since there were no proper controls it's quite difficult to see what the independent variable is.*

4 3

5 Two from:
• to work out the range of measurements needed
• to work out the interval needed between the measurements
• to work out how many measurements to take
• to make sure a method works, to make sure you have the correct apparatus
• to make sure that you have accurate enough measuring apparatus
• to make sure that your investigation is safe.

6 a Each calculation needs to be done this way:
$$\frac{\text{Number who answered a particular way}}{\text{Total number who answered that question}} \times 100 =$$
e.g. 46 people answered 'extremely' to the question 'Was there a reduction in itching?' 63 people in total answered this question. So,
$(46/63) \times 100 = 73\%$

The table shows the rest of the answers:

Was there a reduction in ...	Number who answered	Answered: 'Extremely'	Answered: 'Considerably'	Answered: 'A little'	Answered: 'Not at all'
... itching?	63	73%	24%	3%	0
... pain?	54	89%	11%	0	0
... skin scaliness	66	85%	13%	1%	0

b Your bar chart should have the bars grouped together for each of the three questions.

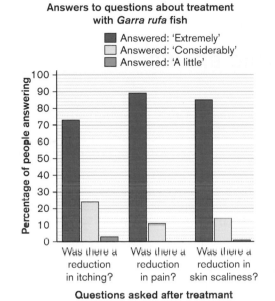

Answers to questions about treatment with *Garra rufa* fish

Key:
- ■ Answered: 'Extremely'
- □ Answered: 'Considerably'
- ■ Answered: 'A little'

Questions asked after treatment

Make sure you have:
- *A title*
- *The dependent variable on the y-axis*
- *The independent variable on the x-axis (In this case the independent variable is the addition of fish and each of the bars shows what happened when the fish were used.)*
- *A good scale for the y-axis so that the plotted points are well spread*
- *A y-axis scale that has even divisions*
- *A y-axis scale that is numbered*
- *A label for the x-axis*
- *Bars grouped together in threes on the x-axis*
- *A label for each group of three bars on the x-axis*
- *Gaps between the x-axis bar groups*
- *All bars accurately plotted*
- *All bars neatly drawn with a ruler*

- *A key to show which bar is which in each group*

The angles you need for the pie charts (see next page) are calculated like this:

Was there a reduction in ... itching?	Answered: 'Extremely'	Answered: 'Considerably'	Answered: 'A little'	Total
percentage	73	24	3	100
angle calculation 360/100 = 3.6	73 × 3.6	24 × 3.6	3 × 3.6	
angle	263°	86°	11°	360°

Was there a reduction in ... pain?	Answered: 'Extremely'	Answered: 'Considerably'	Answered: 'A little'	Total
percentage	89	11	0	100
angle calculation 360/100 = 3.6	89 × 3.6	11 × 3.6	0	
angle	320°	40°		360°

Was there a reduction in ... skin scaliness?	Answered: 'Extremely'	Answered: 'Considerably'	Answered: 'A little'	Total
percentage	85	14	1	100
angle calculation 360/100 = 3.6	85 × 3.6	14 × 3.6	1 × 3.6	
angle	306°	50°	4°	360°

Make sure each pie chart has:
- *The correct angles*
- *A title*
- *All the categories neatly labelled*
- *Lines drawn with a ruler*
- *Circle drawn with a compass or similar*

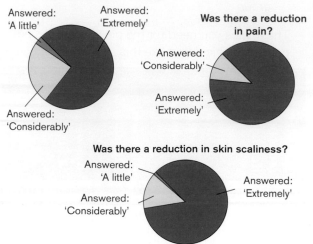

Was there a reduction in itching?

Answered: 'A little'
Answered: 'Extremely'
Answered: 'Considerably'

Was there a reduction in pain?

Answered: 'Considerably'
Answered: 'Extremely'

Was there a reduction in skin scaliness?

Answered: 'A little'
Answered: 'Considerably'
Answered: 'Extremely'

c The bar chart allows a better comparison to be made between the questions.

7 **QWC** *This is a QWC question – see page 76. You need to check your spelling, grammar and punctuation and try to include scientific words, such as 'control', 'data' and 'variable'.*

If a question asks you to explain something then take great care that you <u>explain how</u> something is happening, and you don't just <u>describe what</u> happens.

You should try to include some of the points in the list below. You don't need to make all the points but you should aim to make points with the more stars. If you make 3 or 4 good scientific points in a question like this, and write your answer in good English, you will get 6 marks in an exam. Check your answer with the points below, the grade booster box on page 13 and the general points about QWC answers on page 76.

★weaknesses in the study include: number of fish not controlled, age of patients not controlled, not very many people in the study, there is no control group

★the claim on the website is invalid

★★if not all the control variables are controlled you cannot be sure that you are only measuring the effects of the type of fish (unless you have a control group)

★★there is no control group and so the study assumes that without the fish the people's psoriasis would not improve

★★you can be more sure of the data from bigger studies

★★★the claim on the website is invalid because the study looked at a combination of fish and sunbed, the claim is for the fish-only treatment

★★★without a control group you can't be sure that the fish have any effect (it might be time that makes the psoriasis better, the feeling of being cared for, or the sunbeds)

★★★if the number of fish are not controlled then you can't be sure whether you need a certain number of fish to get a benefit

★★★if ages are not controlled the effects on older and younger people may be different, and so you cannot claim that it will be a beneficial treatment for all ages

★★★anomalous results are more likely to affect the conclusions in a small study because anomalous results will have a greater effect when included in calculations, such as calculating the means

B5 BIG BRAINS

1 a cm^3

b 'centimetres cubed' or 'centimetres × centimetres × centimetres'

2 $650\,cm^3$ and $804\,cm^3$. *This question tests your ability to read off scales but don't forget the units. And notice that the x-axis starts 1 800 000 years ago and you get closer to today as you go left along the axis.*

3 a $1000\,cm^3 - 1300\,cm^3$

b $(1000 + 1030 + 1100 + 1300)/4 = 4430/4 = 1107.5$ $= 1110$ (3 sf) or 1100 (2 sf) *You can't really give your answer to more than 3 significant figures because the figures you've used in the calculation are all given to 3 significant figures or less.* ▲ *Even if you get this answer wrong, you'd still get some credit for the working … and don't forget the units!*

c Plot the means on a scatter graph and use error bars to show the ranges.

4 a quantitative **b** secondary

5 The more recent the skull the bigger its inside volume (a negative correlation between age and volume).

6 **HIGHER** 1.8×10^6

7 a **QWC** People who have only half the amount of brain that is normal are still able to perform the complex tasks that anyone else can. *The* *clue here is to remember to look at all the information on the page, including Figure C*

b *This is quite tricky! An assumption is something that you think is accepted as correct and so you don't try to show that it's correct.* Three possible assumptions (of which you need two) are:

- the bigger a skull is the more brain it will contain
- that bigger brains are needed for more complex behavior
- that the skulls that have been measured are actually from the ancestors of humans.

8 Because the measurements been done by many different scientists who have probably used slightly different ways of measuring the volumes.

9 **QWC** *This is a QWC question – see page 76. You need to check your spelling, grammar and punctuation and try to include scientific words, such as 'evidence', 'data' and 'theory'.*

This question asks you to justify your choice. This means that you have to weigh up the two choices, come to a decision and the use evidence to back up your choice.

You should try to include some of the points in the list below. You don't need to make all the points but you should aim to make points with the more stars. If you make 3 or 4 good scientific points in a question like this, and write your answer in good English, you will get 6 marks in an exam. Check your answer with the points below, the grade booster box on page 15 and the general points about QWC answers on page 76.

★ choose one of the ideas
★ state that the data that shows this is in the scatter graph
★★ describe the shape of the data points in the graph to support a choice
★★ make a reference to how good the data is (which may include the fact that a better judgment could be made if there was more data)
★★★ suggest how one or more 'lines of best fit' could be drawn through the data
★★★ explain how a 'line of best fit' should be drawn and use this to justify your choice of line or lines of best fit to support your argument
★★★ describe the validity of the data (which may include mentioning one or more of the assumptions from question 7b).

B6 PLANTS IN SPACE

1 *In a question like this, there would usually be 1 mark for the explanation and 1 mark for giving an example. But the question asks you to 'illustrate', which means that you can't just state the example, you have to use it as part of your explanation of why a model is useful.*

A model makes a complex idea easier to understand. The chemical equation for photosynthesis shows the reactants and the products without all the very complicated processing that takes place to convert one to the other.

2 Glucose molecules contain 6 carbon atoms, 12 hydrogen atoms and 6 oxygen atoms.

3 Test 3 for green light. It is an anomalous result or outlier and is so way off that it's unlikely to be accurate. If you included it in mean calculations it would alter any conclusions that might be drawn from the results. *Remember that the question asked you to 'explain' so don't simply 'state'.*

4 Red. *They are the readings that are the most closely grouped.*

5 The means are: white – 67 mm³/min, blue 58 mm³/min, 20 mm³/min, 23 mm³/min, 51 mm³/min. *All these are given to 2 significant figures because that's the number of significant figures we have in the data. And the figure for green misses out the anomalous result/outlier because this could have been caused by writing down the figure wrong (e.g. adding a 0 by mistake, making it 180 and not 18).*

6 mm³/min. *This is probably the most useful measurement with the figures that you have got although you could divide everything by 60 to get mm³/s but that's quite a lot of extra work for no real benefit.*

7 You need to draw a bar chart because the independent variable is categoric and the dependent variable is continuous.

You might have included error bars, which are always a nice touch but you won't lose credit for not including them.

Make sure you have:

- *A title*
- *The dependent variable on the y-axis*

- *The independent variable on the x-axis*
- *A good scale for the y-axis so that the plotted points are well spread*
- *A y-axis scale that has even divisions*
- *A y-axis scale that is numbered*
- *A label for the y-axis (with units)*
- *A good scale for the x-axis so that the plotted points are well spread*
- *A label for the x-axis*
- *Gaps between the x-axis bars*
- *The categories correctly labelled on the x-axis*
- *All bars are accurately plotted*
- *All bars are neatly drawn with a ruler (they needn't be coloured)*

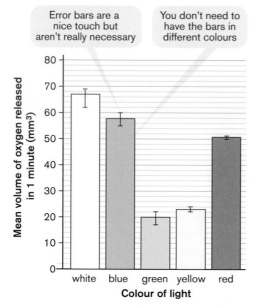

Oxygen released by pond weed in different colours of light

Error bars are a nice touch but aren't really necessary

You don't need to have the bars in different colours

8 *In a question like this, there would usually be 1 mark for the explanation and 1 mark for giving an example. But the question asks you to 'illustrate', which means that you can't just state the example, you have to use it as part of your explanation of why a control is useful.*

The results from the control form a baseline to compare with the other results. In this experiment, the white light is the control. We know that plants grow well in white light and so we can compare the other colours of light against it.

9 **QWC** *This is a QWC question – see page 76. You need to check your spelling, grammar and punctuation and try to include scientific words, such as 'photosynthesis' (including spelling it correctly!).*

When answering questions like this, think about financial costs, effects on people, effects on the environment and ethics. The question asks you to outline, so you could write your answer as a list of points. However, your list needs to be in a logical order and still needs to have accurate spelling, grammar and punctuation.

You should try to include some of the points in the list below. You don't need to make all the points but you should aim to make points with the more stars. If you make 3 or 4 good scientific points in a question like this, and write your answer in good English, you will get 6 marks in an exam. Check your answer with the points below, the grade booster box on page 16 and the general points about QWC answers on page 76.

★ indicate which colour gave the highest numbers/most oxygen

★ glucose is made during photosynthesis and the more of this that can be made in a short period of time the better

★★ the chemical equation tells us that the more oxygen being released by a plant, the faster it is photosynthesising

★★ other factors need to be taken into account such as the cost of the LEDs, the amount of heat they release

★★ in making a decision you need to balance the benefits and the drawbacks

★★★ you need evidence about the costs (e.g. one LED might allow a slightly greater rate of photosynthesis than another but cost a lot more, or have a shorter life-span)

★★★ you need evidence about the other effects of the LED (e.g. one LED might allow a slightly greater rate of photosynthesis than another but produce too much heat, or use much more electricity)

★★★ you need evidence about environmental effects (e.g. will the LED's manufacture damage the environment?)

★★★ you need evidence about safety (e.g. will the LED be safe to use?)

B7 HEALTH SCARE

1 The graphs show a histogram combined with a line graph. *All the data for measles and MMR are combined into 'year groups'. Since it is continuous data you could plot both sets of data as line graphs. Since the data is grouped into years you could also plot both sets of data as*

histograms. Combining a histogram with a line graph can be useful because it makes the two sets of data look different on the graph.

2 A paper that has been checked by an expert in the same subject before being published.

3 a Money. *From the information on the page this is the most likely reason.*

  b There may be bias in his data caused by too few samples/children.

4 a As the numbers of children who are not immunised falls, the cases of measles rise.

  b Yes. There is a good explanation for the correlation – people who are immunised do not get the disease, therefore if fewer people are immunised then it follows that more will get the disease.

5 You could have made any one of these points:
- the study only looked at 12 children (the sample size was too small)
- there was no control group
- it was based on what parents had told him (rather than on experiments)
- out of the 12 of the parents

4 (33%) did not link autism to the MMR vaccination

6 You could have made any one of these points:
- he should not have taken blood at a birthday party by paying children
- you need permission from parents to collect a child's blood and it should be done in a hospital
- he received money from the parents' solicitors but didn't mention that when he published his results

7 Other scientists cannot repeat his findings.

8 **QWC** *This is a QWC question – see page 76. You need to check your spelling, grammar and punctuation and try to include scientific words, such as 'vaccination' or 'immunisation' (including spelling them correctly!).*

If a question asks you to explain something then take great care that you <u>explain how</u> something is happening, and you don't just <u>describe what</u> happens.

You should try to include some of the points in the list below. You don't need to make all the points but you should aim to make points with the more stars. If you make 3 or 4 good scientific points in

a question like this, and write your answer in good English, you will get 6 marks in an exam. Check your answer with the points below, the grade booster box on page 17 and the general points about QWC answers on page 76.

★ reports in the media can change peoples' minds about scientific things

★ many people rely on the media to make sense of science

★ a claim may be widely reported in the media and therefore many people find out about it and start to discuss the subject

★★ a claim might cause panic for no need

★★ Andrew Wakefield's claim that MMR could cause autism meant that many people stopped having their children vaccinated

★★★ Andrew Wakefield's claim that MMR vaccinations could cause autism led to more children getting measles

★★★ some media stories about Andrew Wakefield's claim did not question his paper or his claims with the result that there was an over-reaction by people

B8 CLONES

1

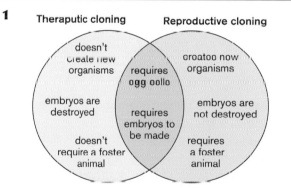

Theraputic cloning — Reproductive cloning

doesn't create new organisms
requires egg cells
create new organisms
embryos are destroyed
requires embryos to be made
embryos are not destroyed
doesn't require a foster animal
requires a foster animal

2 *Make sure you include all the information. Your table should look something like this:*

Mammal	Name	Attempts needed to clone it	Year of cloning
Sheep	Dolly	277	1996
Cat	CC	188	2001

3 5% or 0.05

4 Benefits: they may get another very fast greyhound

Drawbacks: very high cost, may not work, the cloned greyhound may not be very fast, it may not live long

5 They are going to benefit from the research or believe that the research is very important. *Note that the word donation means 'free'!*

6 There is a hazard of the needle used to collect the eggs causing an infection. It is sterile to reduce the risk of this happening.

7 Cloning research raises questions about what is wrong and what is right. What individuals think is right or wrong are their morals. What a group of people agrees on as being right or wrong are ethics.

8 **QWC** *This is a QWC question – see page 76. You need to check your spelling, grammar and punctuation and try to include scientific words, such as 'embryo'.*

This question asks you to justify your opinion. This means that you have to weigh up the pros and cons of reproductive cloning and then reach an opinion about this. You then need to back up your opinion with evidence.

You should try to include some of the points in the list below. You don't need to make all the points but you should aim to make points with the more stars. If you make 3 or 4 good scientific points in a question like this, and write your answer in good English, you will get 6 marks in an exam. Check your answer with the points below, the grade booster box on page 19 and the general points about QWC answers on page 76.

★ state that you think it is a good thing or a bad thing with some idea of why
★ include some comment about others not agreeing and why they may not agree
★★ points in favour of reproductive cloning include: could help parents replace a lost child, could help infertile couples have a baby, would increase our knowledge of human development
★★ points against reproductive cloning include: difficult to get to work, clones would not be sure of their identity, clones may have abonormality, clones may die young, clones may not behave in the way expected/wanted
★★★ argument is structured, complete with counterarguments and a summary
★★★ evidence is given for believing points for and against: difficult to get to work (CC needed 188 attempts, Dolly needed 277), clones may die young (Dolly died at half the normal age for a sheep), could help parents replace a lost child (having an exact copy would help to heal the grief since it could be like having the original child back again)

1 Why is the number of people who get malignant melanoma increasing?

2 a **QWC** The levels of malignant melanoma depend on the number of holidays abroad.

b One of:
- there is not very much data
- you need more than 6 years to be sure of the trend
- the data does not show that the people who go on more holidays abroad are the ones that are getting more malignant melanomas

3 Compare only the years 2003 to 2005, when the ozone levels are falling (which means that there will be more UV reaching the Earth). *Not showing all the data is a common way of biasing evidence.*

4 a **HIGHER** 6.95×10^7. *The number from the graph is 69.5 million, which is 69 500 000. You need to move the decimal point 7 places to the left in order to get only one digit in front of it.*
🔺 *You'll get credit for showing your working, even if you misread the graph.*

b 2.7 million holidays per year (or 2 700 000 holidays per year). *Don't forget to read the scales properly. In this case the y-axis is in 'millions' and it's easy not to spot this. The rate of increase is the slope of a straight line between the point for 2003 and the point for 2006 on the graph. This is worked out by calculating the amount of change of the y-variable and diving this by the amount of change of the x-variable.*

$(69.5 - 61.4)/(2006 - 2003) = 8.1/3 = 2.7$ million holidays per year

5 *You'll have needed a ruler for this, to see a line of best through the points.*
- for 2002, any number between 11.4 and 11.8
- for 2009, any number between 16.8 and 17.2

6 Benefit: helps the skin to make vitamin A.

Drawbacks: skin cancer/malignant melanoma/sunburn.
Risk: risk of malignant melanoma is 1 in 77 for women or 1 in 91 for men. *Remember that really the risk should be linked to the drawback.*

7 1.1% *There is a 1 in 91 chance, which can be written as 1/91. You multiply the result by 100 to get the percentage. And since the data you are using are to two significant figures your answer should be too.*

8 **QWC** *This is a QWC question – see page 76. You need to check your spelling, grammar and punctuation and try to include scientific words, such as 'melanoma' (including spelling it correctly!).*

You should try to include some of the points in the list below. You don't need to make all the points but you should aim to make points with the more stars. If you make 3 or 4 good scientific points in a question like this, and write your answer in good English, you will get 6 marks in an exam. Check your answer with the points below, the grade booster box on page 20 and the general points about QWC answers on page 76.

★ run a survey where you ask people how long they use a sunbed for on average each month or find secondary data that contains this information

★ include in the survey a question about whether the people have or have not had malignant melanoma or find secondary data that contains this information

★ see if there are more cases of melanoma in people who use sunbeds more

★★ the group of people who have never used sunbeds is the control

★★ a control is when the independent (input) variable is not applied

★★ a control lets you see if changes are only due to the independent (input) variable

★★ divide the data for those who use sunbeds into groups, depending on the number of hours spent on the sunbed

★★★ calculate the probability that a person in a group will get a malignant melanoma

★★★ use a histogram to spot a correlation

★★★ calculate the probability of someone in the control group getting malignant melanoma and see whether the probabilities in the other groups are higher than this

B10 BMI

1 a *BMI is calculated using metres and not centimetres, so you first need to convert 181 cm to 1.81 m.* BMI = $99/1.81^2$ = $99/(1.81 \times 1.81)$ = 30.2 so Derek is obese.

b **HIGHER** BMI = $43/1.36^2$ = $43/(1.36 \times 1.36)$ = 23.2 so (from Figure B) Jane is overweight.

All these answers are given to 3 significant figures because that's the number of significant figures we have in the data. And don't forget that you need to use the table for 1a and Figure B for 1b because of the ages of the people.

2 a 'square metres' or 'metres squared'

b area

3 A rough calculation. *A BMI cannot be any more than an estimate because your mass varies from day to day depending on when you last ate, the time of day, etc.*

4 Any one of: number of clothes children are wearing when having their masses measured, the time of day they are measured, the time of year they are measured, the resolution of the 'scales' used, the accuracy of the scales used.

5 If a large number of measurements is missing it can cause bias. *Think about it this way. If the reason most of the people who didn't want to be measured was because they were embarrassed about their masses, then there will be a large number of overweight people whose masses are not used in the graph. This will mean that there is bias towards lighter people.*

6 The more wealthy people are, the less likely they are to be obese. *If you plotted a graph of 'wealth' on the x-axis against 'obesity' on the y-axis, the line of best fit would slope downwards.*

7 **QWC** *This is a QWC question – see page 76. You need to check your spelling, grammar and punctuation and try to include scientific words, such as 'nutritious' (including spelling it correctly!).*

The question needs you to make two suggestions: one for why the company advertised it in that way and the other for why it was banned.

You should try to include some of the points in the list below. You don't need to make all the points but you should aim to make points with the more stars. If you make 3 or 4 good scientific points in a question like this, and write your answer in good English, you will get 6 marks in an exam. Check your answer with the points below, the grade booster box on page 21 and the general points about QWC answers on page 76.

★ the company wanted to encourage people to buy the drink

★ the drink contains vitamins and your body needs vitamins

★ the drink contains sugar, which your body needs

★★ the word 'nutritious' makes the drink sound healthy

★★ people do not expect something that is healthy to contain so much sugar

★★ consuming too much sugar over a long period can help to cause obesity/diabetes

★★★ there is no evidence to support the claim that the product is actually good for you

★★★ drinking so much sugar in one serving is not good for you because it means you are likely to consume too much sugar in a day

★★★ anything that is nutritious contains sources of energy-supply substances and substances needed for health, which this product contains

C1 MEMORY OF WATER

1 a To make complex ideas easier to understand.

b Good: it shows the number of atoms in the water molecule, it shows how the atoms in a water molecule are arranged, it shows which atoms are found in a water molecule.
Poor: the atoms don't have those colours, the atoms are not joined with 'sticks'.

2 2:1 *Make sure you write it this way round.*

3 Mix one volume of the original chemical with nine volumes of water to make a 10 × dilution. Take one volume of the 10 × dilution and mix it with nine volumes of water to make a 100 × dilution. Take one volume of the 100 × dilution and mix it with nine volumes of water to make a 1000 × dilution (1×10^3). Take one volume of the 1000 × dilution and mix it with nine volumes of water to make a 10 000 × dilution (1×10^4). OR Take one volume of the original and mix it with 9999 volumes of water. OR Take one volume of the original and mix it with 99 volumes of water to form a 100 × dilution and then take 1 volume of the 100 × dilution and mix that with 99 volumes of water. *There are lots of*

ways of doing this. Just make sure that you understand that a 1×10^4 dilution means 1 part in 10 000, which is the same as saying 1 volume of the original mixed with 9999 parts of water forming a total of 10 000.

4 a Any answer between 1:1.8 and 1:1.9 for the ratio of the range of the graph on the left to that of the one on the right. You need to divide the range of the second graph (which is 73 – 0) by the range of the first graph (40 – 0). 73/40 = 1.8. So the ratio tells you that the range of the second graph is 1.8 times bigger than the range of the first.

b They show that when the person counting the cells does not know which dilution the cells have been in, the experiment does not work as expected. For instance, in the left-hand graph there is a peek at '6'. On the right-hand graph this is a trough.

5 Two from: type of cells, type of water used, chemical used, containers in which chemicals/cells were mixed, method of counting cells without granules.

6 Neither he nor the reviewers could find any fault with the method and the results as they were set out in the paper. *This doesn't mean that there wasn't something wrong, just that nobody could tell what was wrong.*

7 **QWC** *This is a QWC question – see page 76. You need to check your spelling, grammar and punctuation and try to include scientific words, such as 'error' and 'bias'.*

The question asks you to use information from the page. You may not get any marks if you don't do this.

You should try to include some of the points in the list below. You don't need to make all the points but you should aim to make points with the more stars. If you make 3 or 4 good scientific points in a question like this, and write your answer in good English, you will get 6 marks in an exam. Check your answer with the points below, the grade booster box on page 22 and the general points about QWC answers on page 76.

★ the person counting the cells made mistakes

★ this is called human error

★★ the results in the paper show systematic error

★★ the results from the two graphs in Figure B

show random error

★★ the results shown in the paper show bias

★★★ the person counting the cells was convinced that certain dilutions had effects on the cells and so subconsciously counted more cells without granules in those dilutions compared to dilutions that she didn't think had an effect

★★★ by leaving out the results from experiments that don't work, you create bias shifting all the results in a certain direction

★★★ the peaks are bigger than they should be, since they are calculated from means of measurements but without the results from experiments that didn't work

C2 THE PERIODIC TABLE

1 He predicted:

- elements that had not yet been discovered
- that some of the 'atomic weights' were wrong

QWC *You could have used the 'if … then …' phrase in your answer:*

- *If there are gaps when elements with similar properties are put together, then there must be undiscovered elements to fill those gaps.*
- *If two elements are in order of their 'atomic weight' but don't match the properties of the element above them, then their 'atomic weights' are wrong.*

2 It did not explain all the data (he left out half of the known elements).

3 a Ga (gallium). *You'll have needed to look this up in the periodic table on page 126.*

b Mendeleev had predicted that this element would be found and so this supports his theory/idea.

c The graph shows that elements follow a pattern when put in 'atomic weight' order. This is the same pattern that Mendeleev found. *Or you could have mentioned that Lothar Meyer reached the same conclusion as Mendeleev but was working independently.*

4 a line graph

b The mass could be measured in grams or milligrams and the volume in cm^3 or mm^3.

5 a secondary

b One of: you have no control over the quality of the data, it doesn't cost you much money or time to obtain it, it's easy to obtain.

6 One of: they are quick to write and so often clearer, they aren't affected by different names/spellings in different countries, all scientists across the world understand instantly what they mean.

7 You should have 602 with 21 zeros after it.

8 **QWC** *This is a QWC question – see page 76. You need to check your spelling, grammar and punctuation and try to include scientific words, such as 'journal' and 'paper'.*

This question has two parts. The first part wants you to describe a process and so you will need to write what happens in a logical way. The other part wants you to talk about the benefits, so you need to refer to your description of the process and pick out the parts that are beneficial.

You should try to include some of the points in the list below. You don't need to make all the points but you should aim to make points with the more stars. If you make 3 or 4 good scientific points in a question like this, and write your answer in good English, you will get 6 marks in an exam. Check your answer with the points below, the grade booster box on page 23 and the general points about QWC answers on page 76.

★ a scientist's paper is checked by other scientists

★ this means that the reader can be more sure that the paper contains good science

★★ paper is sent to a journal

★★ editor of the journal sends it out to other experts in the same field

★★ comments from experts mean that the paper is published, amended and then published or not published

★★ a reader does not have to carefully analyse the paper for mistakes since this has been done by experts

★★★ the investigations are evaluated to ensure that the results are valid

★★★ the conclusions are checked to make sure they can be drawn from the results

★★★ the reviewer looks out for bias

1 a 92.5 %

b *You need to have drawn a pie chart for this data because you are showing the different proportions that contribute to a whole.*

The angles you need for the pie chart are calculated as follows.

Element	Al	Si	Mg	Total
percentage	92.5	7.1	0.4	100
angle calculation 360/100 = 3.6	92.5 × 3.6	7.1 × 3.6	0.4 × 3.6	
angle	333°	26°	1°	360°

Make sure each pie chart has:
- *The correct angles*
- *A title*
- *All the categories neatly labelled*
- *Lines drawn with a ruler*
- *Circle drawn with a compass or similar*

Percentages of elements in an aluminium alloy

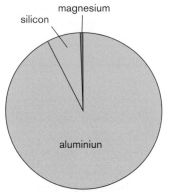

2 Two from: keep the testing machine the same, use the same shape of alloy bar each time, increase the force on the bar at the same rate for each bar.

3 a 40 kN (or 40 000 N). *You'll have needed to extend the line of best fit to the y-axis.*

b 69.4 kN and 55.5 kN because they do not sit close to the line of best fit like the other measurements.

4 56 000 N, 69 000 N, 71 000 N, 80 000 N, 97 000 N
Don't forget that the question wanted the answer in newtons and not kilonewtons.

5 a Volume = 1 × 2 × 2 = 4 cm³. Density = mass/volume = 32/4 = 8 g/cm³

b Density = mass/volume and so mass = density × volume = 2.7 × 4 = 10.8 g. OR Use ratios: mass = (2.7/8) x 32 = 10.8 g. *Don't forget the unit in your answer.*

6 The benefit is that they are lighter than normal/ steel wheels. The drawback is that they are more expensive. *You might be able to think up other benefits and drawbacks but these are the ones given on the page.*

7 **QWC** *This is a QWC question – see page 76. You need to check your spelling, grammar and punctuation and try to include scientific words, such as 'valid'.*

The question asks you to evaluate a number of things – the conclusions. So you need to compare the different conclusions pointing out their good and bad points before choosing one conclusion and saying why you have chosen that one.

You should try to include some of the points in the list below. You don't need to make all the points but you should aim to make points with the more stars. If you make 3 or 4 good scientific points in a question like this, and write your answer in good English, you will get 6 marks in an exam. Check your answer with the points below, the grade booster box on page 24 and the general points about QWC answers on page 76.

★ conclusion ii selected
★ points out that two conclusions are for a crane hook and one is for a bridge support
★ points out that two conclusions are for 7.5% manganese
★ points out that 7.5% manganese is the strongest alloy that was tested
★★ points out that the test is for stretching the bar and not squashing it
★★ points out that 7.5% manganese was the highest proportion of manganese tested
★★ points out that conclusions i and iii are invalid
★★★ dismisses conclusion i because the strength of the bar when squashed is not tested
★★★ dismisses conclusion iii because the conclusion is not based on the test results. *It's impossible to say that the bar keeps on getting stronger the more manganese you add to it. From the results that you have, you could predict that this will be the case but you would need to test it before you can draw that conclusion.*

1 a MPa, megapascals

  b 1 megapascal is 1 000 000 pascals, or you could explain that 1 pascal is the same as the force of 1 N on 1 m^2.

2 a The greater the temperature the less ammonia formed.

  b negative

3

Pressure (MPa)	Percentage of ammonia formed (%)
20	19
30	27
41	32
51	36.5

Your table should be in order of pressure or in order of percentage of ammonia formed .... as long as it has an order!

4 a It's poisonous or high pressures might cause an explosion

  b Make sure that the ammonia is always carefully contained and cannot escape or make sure the reaction vessel is very strong. *Make sure you understand the difference between a hazard and a risk*

5 a percentage ammonia formed, pressure, temperature

  b percentage ammonia: dependent, quantitative, continuous
  pressure: independent, quantitative, continuous
  temperature: independent, quantitative, continuous

6 You should try to include some of the following points:

  • a balance between speed, expense and percentage of ammonia formed must be reached
  • although the temperature could be lower to increase the percentage of ammonia, this makes the reaction too slow
  • although the pressure could be higher, this requires more expensive equipment and the increase in percentage isn't worth it

7 **QWC** *This is a QWC question – see page 76. You need to check your spelling, grammar and punctuation and try to include scientific words, such as 'ammonia' and 'Haber process'.*

The question asks you to write an argument. So you first need to plan out what points you are going to make and what points others might use to argue against you.

You should try to include some of the points in the list below. You don't need to make all the points but you should aim to make points with the more stars. If you make 3 or 4 good scientific points in a question like this, and write your answer in good English, you will get 6 marks in an exam. Check your answer with the points below, the grade booster box on page 25 and the general points about QWC answers on page 76.

★ states that you are in favour of the factory
★ gives a reason for being in favour of the factory (e.g. it will improve local facilities, it will provide jobs)
★★ explains one or more reasons against the factory (e.g. noise will be caused by transport to and from the factory, building work will destroy habitats for animals and plants, ammonia is poisonous and might leak)
★★ explains one or more reasons in favour of the factory (e.g. it will improve local facilities because that factory will need to build new roads/houses/facilities for the workers, the factory will need people to run it and so it will provide jobs)
★★★ writes an argument with the same structure as shown in S41
★★★ uses personal knowledge to back up reasons in favour of the factory (e.g. it will provide jobs because whenever something new opens they need people to operate the machinery and this factory is new to the area – it's not replacing something that was already there)
★★★ writes a clear response to one counterargument (e.g. some people might say that ammonia is made to make dangerous explosives but the explosives will not be made at the factory and most ammonia is used to make fertilisers which are important)

C5 RIVER QUALITY

1 Qualitative: grades; quantitative: either the percentage oxygen or the ammonia concentration.

2 A molecule (or unit) of ammonia contains 1 nitrogen atom and 3 hydrogen atoms.

3 less than

4 mg/dm^3 is a compound measure. *Remember that a compound measure is nothing to do with chemical 'compounds' – it is a measuring unit made by combining other units.*

5 A total of 36 readings gives a good number of samples which means that the results are less likely to be biased by anomalous results.

6 Chemical fertilisers increase ammonia levels in rivers and so can harm water creatures. Also chemical fertilisers cause algae growth, which causes problems when the algae die because the bacteria that break them down use up a lot of the oxygen, meaning there is much less for other water creatures.

7 **HIGHER**

a No, because they vary a lot (for example, the readings for dissolved oxygen vary from 75 or below to 94 or above).

b **QWC** *This is a QWC question – see page 76. You need to check your spelling, grammar and punctuation and try to include scientific words, such as 'percentile'.*

This question asks you to state something so make sure that you give short and accurate meanings before grading the river. It then asks you to explain how you do something, so make sure that you explain all the steps in how you would use these figures to work out a grade for the river.

You should try to include some of the points in the list below. You don't need to make all the points but you should aim to make points with the more stars. If you make 3 or 4 good scientific points in a question like this, and write your answer in good English, you will get 6 marks in an exam. Check your answer with the points below, the grade booster box on page 26 and the general points about QWC answers on page 76.

★ a grade of A or B is given (A isn't correct but very nearly is.)

★ the ammonia readings for the river are all under the $0.25\,mg/dm^3$ limit for a grade A

★★ the dissolved oxygen is 79% at the 10th percentile but needs to be 80% for a grade A

★★ the dissolved oxygen percentage scores the river a grade B but the ammonia concentration scores a grade A. The overall grade is the lower of the two (i.e. B).

★★★ a percentile is the cut-off point for a certain percentage of all the readings (or is the measurement at or below which a certain percentage of readings fall)

★★★ a 10th percentile is the reading at the 10% level of all the measurements, cutting off the bottom 10% of all readings OR a 90th percentile is cutting off the bottom 90% of all readings

★★★ for a grade A for dissolved oxygen, only 10% of readings can be below 80%

★★★ for a grade A for ammonia, 90% of readings must be below $0.25\,mg/dm^3$

C6 EARTH MOVING

1 a One of: Why are rocks in South America the same as those in Africa? Why are fossils from South America the same as those in Africa? Why does the shape of South America seem to fit into Africa?

b **QWC** The position of the continents depends on the amount of time that they have been moving. *Or you could have written 'the continents were moving'. You don't have to use 'depends on' but it often helps you to write a hypothesis correctly.*

c **QWC** Predictions include:

- you could measure the speed of the continents moving
- a continent would not stay in the same position if you measured it at two different points in time

You could also phrase these using 'if … then …' phrases. For example: If we measure the position of a place on a continent at two different points in time, then we will see that the place has moved.

d It allowed predictions to be made (e.g. that continents were moving), explained all the observations (e.g. the observations in Figure A), explained other observations that weren't thought to be linked to the theory (e.g. why there were sea-creature fossils up in the mountains).

e Two continents pushed into each other and the Earth rose up, lifting the fossils into their current position.

2 The resolution (sensitivity) of the instruments was not good enough.

3 mm or cm 'per year' or 'per decade' or perhaps 'per month'

4 Marcou was a geologist but Wegener was not.

5

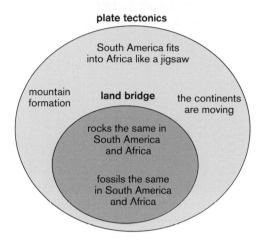

6 **QWC** *There are some examples of answers to this question, and comments on those answers, on pages 78–79. This is a QWC question – see page 76. You need to check your spelling, grammar and punctuation and try to include scientific words, such as 'continental drift' and 'plate tectonics'.*

The question asks you to write a short article. So you first need to plan out what points you are going to make and then arrange them into a structure as shown in S49.

You should try to include some of the points in the list below. You don't need to make all the points but you should aim to make points with the more stars. If you make 3 or 4 good scientific points in a question like this, and write your answer in good English, you will get 6 marks in an exam. Check your answer with the points below, the grade booster box on page 27 and the general points about QWC answers on page 76.

★ describe the theory of 'continental drift'
★ state one or more observations that supported 'continental drift'
★ state one or more objections to 'continental drift'

★ state one or more reasons why the objections are no longer thought to be true
★ state that finding the plates on the Earth's crust altered the theory
★ state that finding the Earth's plates were moving altered the theory
★ state that 'plate tectonics' is based on Wegener's 'continental drift'
★★ arrange your article so that you start with an overview paragraph
★★ arrange your article so that you follow the opening with a series of points, each of which has some details and some evidence to support it
★★ arrange your article so that each point has its own paragraph
★★ arrange your article so that it ends with a concluding paragraph, giving a summary
★★★ 'plate tectonics' explains how continents are moved on huge cracked plates in the Earth's crust
★★★ 'continental drift' could not explain how continents could move across the sea floor

C7 EARTH WARMING

1 You need to draw a histogram because, for the x-axis, you are using continuous data that has been chunked into groups.

Make sure you have:

- *A title*
- *The dependent variable on the y-axis*
- *The independent variable on the x-axis*
- *A good scale for the y-axis so that the plotted points are well spread*
- *A y-axis scale that has even divisions*
- *A y-axis scale that is numbered*
- *A label for the y-axis*
- *A good scale for the x-axis so that the bars are wide*
- *A label for the x-axis*
- *No gaps between the x-axis bars*
- *An x-axis scale that has even divisions*
- *The categories correctly labelled on the x-axis (you may have drawn a scale as shown overleaf or labelled these groups on the x-axis as '1980–1989', '1990–1999', '2000–2009')*
- *All bars accurately plotted*
- *All bars neatly drawn with a ruler*

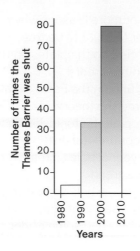

2 A line graph has been drawn for the left-hand graph because both variables are continuous. A bar chart has been drawn for the right-hand chart because one variable is categoric.

3 A way of thinking about something using a computer, which makes things easier for us to understand.

4 a It's quicker/easier just to use one set of data.

b One data set is unlikely to reflect the same conditions as elsewhere in the world and so will produce bias in the models.

c Collect CO_2 data from many places around the world, and locate those places at random.

5 The graph is a fairly straight line so pick two points that are easy to read off it to calculate the gradient e.g.

$$\frac{(80-60)}{(95-81)} = \frac{20}{14} = 1.4\,\text{ppm/year}$$

6 a 1 in 1000 is $1/1000 = 0.001$. To get a percentage multiply by $100 = 0.1\%$.

b The risk is halved. So, $0.1 \div 2 = 0.05\%$

c 0.2%. *A tricky one!* If the barrier halves the risk but by 2030 the reduced risk is back to today's risk, then the risk has doubled. So if the Thames Barrier had not been built, the risk of London flooding in 2030 is twice what it is today without the Thames Barrier.

7 The cost of building it was very much less than the cost of the city flooding.

8 **QWC** *This is a QWC question – see page 76. You need to check your spelling, grammar and punctuation and try to include scientific words, such as 'risk'.*

This question asks you to explain something so

make sure you <u>explain how</u> the page does or does not make a good magazine article; don't just <u>describe what</u> is on the page or how the article is structured.

You should try to include some of the points in the list below. You don't need to make all the points but you should aim to make points with the more stars. If you make 3 or 4 good scientific points in a question like this, and write your answer in good English, you will get 6 marks in an exam. Check your answer with the points below, the grade booster box on page 29 and the general points about QWC answers on page 76.

★ the article isn't balanced
★ there is little evidence presented for global warming
★ there are no sources of data given
★ information is up to date
★ spelling and grammar are good
★★ articles should present both sides of a debate and so there should be something in here about other reasons why the barrier might be being opened more often or other reasons why global temperatures may be increasing
★★ the only evidence presented for global warming is that the sea levels are rising (as shown by the increasing number of times that the Thames Barrier is shut). But sea levels could be rising due to something else and there is no evidence presented that directly links carbon dioxide levels to increases in global temperatures.
★★ data sources should be stated in an article
★★★ if an article presents both sides of a debate then you can understand why the writer is arguing for a certain point of view
★★★ if there is little evidence given then there is no reason for a reader to believe what the article says
★★★ if the data sources are not stated there is no way for a reader to check that the information given in the article is accurate or true

C8 AIRBAGS

1 0.03 seconds. *The question wants your answer in seconds and not milliseconds.*

2 … decompose/break apart/go to give 2 atoms/units of sodium and 2 molecules/units of nitrogen. *To be technical, sodium azide is an ionic solid and so you can't refer to it as 'molecules'. This is why the first part of the* answer contained the word 'units'. If you've learnt about moles you could use 'moles' instead of 'units'. Sodium exists as atoms. Nitrogen exists as molecules of two nitrogen atoms bonded together.

3 a Three from: to work out the range of measurements to take, to work out the intervals needed between each measurement, to work out how many measurements to take, to work out how many repeat readings to take, to make sure that you don't make unnecessary readings in the full investigation, to make sure that your method works, to make sure that you have the correct apparatus, to make sure you have accurate enough measuring apparatus, to make sure the method is safe.

b Mass of gas, temperature. *Look at the graph title and the caption.*

4 a The reading at 40 dm³. This reading is anomalous/doesn't fit the pattern.

b **HIGHER** volume is inversely proportional to pressure (or vice versa), for a fixed mass. $P \propto 1/V$ or $V \propto 1/P$.

c **HIGHER** Plot pressure against 1/V (or volume against 1/P).

5 The volume of a cylinder is $\pi \times r^2 \times h$. The height is 26 cm and the radius is 58/2 = 29 cm. So the volume = 3.142 × (29 × 29) × 26 = 68 700 cm³ which is about 69 dm³. From the graph, an airbag of 69 dm³ would give a pressure of about 42 kPa. The bag needs to be bigger.

6 Two from: look at the evidence from countries where airbags are compulsory to see if there are problems; look at the figures to see if airbags save lives/prevent injuries; check that airbags don't make cars too expensive; look at the effect of airbags on the environment; look at the effects of airbags going off by mistake.

7 **QWC** *This is a QWC question – see page 76. You need to check your spelling, grammar and punctuation and try to include scientific words, such as 'sodium azide'.*

This question asks you to discuss something, which means that you need to build up an argument about whether it is a good idea or not to fit airbags in cars. You will need to think about the benefits, drawbacks and risks and then put your ideas down in the form of an argument (see S41).

You should try to include some of the points in the list below. You don't need to make all the points but you should aim to make points with the more stars. If you make 3 or 4 good scientific points in a question like this, and write your answer in good English, you will get 6 marks in an exam. Check your answer with the points below, the grade booster box on page 30 and the general points about QWC answers on page 76.

★ identify one benefit of airbags (e.g. an airbag helps to protect people in cars from injury in a car crash, helps to reduce the costs to the NHS)
★ identify one drawback of airbags (e.g. contains a poisonous chemical, may go off accidentally, makes a car cost more)
★ identify one way in which risks are reduced (e.g. putting sodium azide in a strong container, setting the correct volume of the airbag)
★ state that you are in favour of or against airbags, with a reason
★★ explain two or more benefits of airbags (e.g. airbags help protect people in cars from injury in a car crash by inflating very quickly to stop a person hitting the dashboard/steering wheel, help to reduce the costs to the NHS through making injuries less serious)
★★ explain two or more drawbacks of airbags (e.g. contains a poisonous chemical that can stop people breathing, may go off accidentally leading to an accident because the driver can't see or gets a fright, makes a car cost more due to the materials used to make airbags and additional time required to fit the airbags)
★★ explain two or more ways in which risks are reduced (e.g. fitting airbags reduces the risk of injury in a car crash, putting sodium azide in a strong container reduces the risk of it escaping and so coming into contact with someone, setting the correct volume of the airbag to ensure correct pressure so that the airbag works without injuring someone)
★★★ the risk of kidney injury in a car crash is 139/2864 = 0.049, or 4.9%
★★★ the risk of kidney injury with an airbag is 43/2864 = 0.015, or 1.5%
★★★ the risk of kidney injury with an airbag is reduced by 1.5/4.9 = 0.31, or 31%
★★★ an argument written with the same structure as show on S41
★★★ a clear response given to one counterargument

C9 AVOGADRO'S BIG IDEA

1 3:1

2 a e.g. g/cm³, g/dm³, kg/m³. *You can have a variety of units here, as long as it is a compound measure consisting of a mass unit divided by a volume unit.*

b 1.10, 0.0732

c 1.10/0.0732 = 15.0

d Today the relative atomic mass of oxygen is one unit greater (16). Or, today the relative atomic mass oxygen is 7% bigger. *You can't just write '16' as your answer because the question has asked you to compare two figures. To calculate a percentage increase, work out the size of the increase and divide it by the original amount and then multiply by 100. So (16–15)/15 × 100 = 7%.*

3 Your model should look like Figure A but show: i) hydrogen particles composed of two atoms of hydrogen stuck together, ii) oxygen particles composed of two atoms of oxygen stuck together, iii) two volumes of water.

4

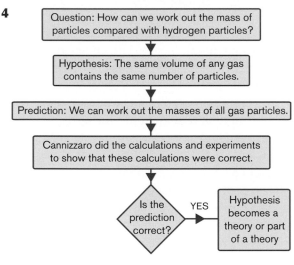

5 Avogadro wasn't very well known and Berzelius was very influential, so people believed him and not Avogadro. Or, he didn't do enough experiments to support his hypothesis.

6 You need to have drawn a scatter graph here to compare the two variables and draw a line of best fit. From the line of best fit you can calculate its gradient, which will be the volume of gas per mole.

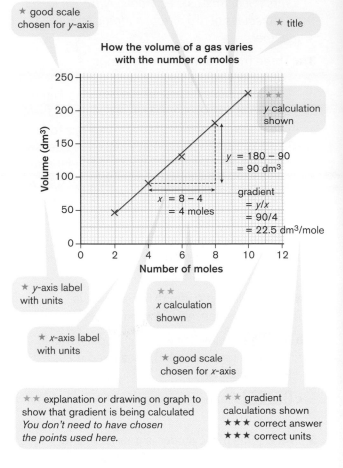

C10 COLD PACKS

1 0.1 °C

2 Don't touch/wear gloves and be careful not to raise the dust/don't breathe in the dust/wear a face mask when handling.

3 a The reading of 15.2 °C is well away from all the others.

b 7.6, 8.4, 9.2 (ignoring the anomalous result), 10.8, 10.2

c You need to have drawn a scatter graph because you are looking for relationships/correlations between two quantitative and continuous variables.

You might have tried a line of best fit for the first 4 points, although this isn't really useful here because the last point doesn't fit the pattern and is not an anomalous result because all the readings for 6 g of sodium nitrate were pretty much the same. It's at this point that you have to think about extending the range of the masses of sodium nitrate used to see what happens to the temperature drop then.

You might have included error bars, which are always a nice touch but you won't lose credit for not including them.

Make sure you have:

- *A title*
- *The dependent variable on the y-axis (temperature change)*
- *The independent variable on the x-axis (mass of sodium nitrate)*
- *A good scale for the y-axis so that the plotted points are well spread*
- *A y-axis scale that has even divisions*
- *A y-axis scale that is numbered*
- *A label for the y-axis with units*
- *A good scale for the x-axis so that the plotted points are well spread*
- *A label for the x-axis with units*
- *An x-axis scale that has even divisions*
- *An x-axis scale that is numbered*
- *All points are accurately plotted*
- *All points are neatly plotted*
- *(A line of best fit drawn using a ruler, if you've done one)*

Relationship between the mass of sodium nitrate added and the temperature change

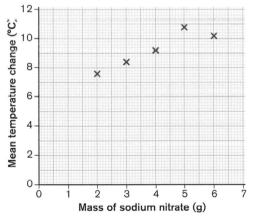

d The more sodium nitrate used the greater the change in temperature.

4 Two from: the apparatus, the starting temperature, the chemicals used, the amount of water added, the amount of ammonium chloride used.

5 More readings need to be taken. The last reading (at 6 g) does not fit the rest of the pattern. This could be anomalous or the change in temperature could have started going down with increasing mass of sodium nitrate. You cannot tell.

6 **QWC** The cooling ability of a cold pack depends on the chemicals inside it. *That's the hypothesis that the investigation was intended to test. But, if you look at the table, that's not what the investigation actually tested.*

7 **QWC** *This is a QWC question – see page 76. You need to check your spelling, grammar and punctuation and try to include scientific words, such as the correct terms for the units.*

This question asks you to evaluate a single thing. So you need to say how good or poor the investigation is based on the list of things to check given in S42.

You should try to include some of the points in the list below. You don't need to make all the points but you should aim to make points with the more stars. If you make 3 or 4 good scientific points in a question like this, and write your answer in good English, you will get 6 marks in an exam. Check your answer with the points below, the grade booster box on page 32 and the general points about QWC answers on page 76.

★ the data is good because the measurements have been repeated
★ the data is precise because repeated measurements (apart from one) are quite close
★ the conclusion does not match the hypothesis
★ the heading in the table 'change in temperature' is not good because it doesn't tell you whether the change is up or down
★★ the investigation is not valid
★★ the measuring devices were accurate enough for this investigation
★★ there is bias in all the '1st try' readings, which are all slightly on the high side
★★★ the results were accurate enough to draw a conclusion because the changes in the readings are much greater than the resolution of the measuring devices
★★★ the investigation is not valid because the investigation does not test lots of different chemicals
★★★ the only conclusion that can be drawn from these results is that ammonium chloride is better to use in cold backs than sodium nitrate. *This is a difficult one to get! Have a look at the graph you drew for question 3. If you draw and extend a line of best fit (missing out the last point) so that it meets the y-axis, you will see that with no sodium nitrate the temperature change is about 5 °C. This is caused by 2.5 g of ammonium*

chloride. 2.5 g of sodium nitrate causes an additional temperature decrease of 2.9 °C (about 7.9 °C in total). So ammonium chloride is more effective than sodium nitrate. However, this conclusion doesn't really mean this is a good investigation of the hypothesis – there are too few chemicals tested.

P1 COLD FUSION

1 Benefits: electricity without smoke pollution/ without carbon dioxide; drawbacks: produces radioactive waste.

2 a **QWC** Based on the information on this page you could have any one of three hypotheses: The ability of deuterium to fuse at room temperature depends on the amount of D_2O/the volume of palladium/the substance used to absorb it. *You don't have to use 'depends on' but it often helps you to write a hypothesis correctly.*

b **QWC** Two from:
- if deuterium fuses then heat would be produced
- if deuterium fuses then helium would be produced
- if deuterium fuses then protons or neutrons or gamma rays would be produced.

3 **HIGHER** 1.5×10^7

4 To allow time for peer review or to allow time for other scientists to check the work.

5 a They broke their agreement with Steven E. Jones.

b Two from:
- they couldn't explain how their experiment was working
- there was no control
- other scientists could not repeat the results
- there was no helium produced (which would be predicted by the theory)
- there were no neutrons produced (which would be predicted by the theory)
- there were no protons produced (which would be predicted by the theory)
- there were no gamma rays produced

6 The thermometer was only measuring the temperature in one part of the apparatus, which got warmer during the experiment. The liquid was colder in other parts but they assumed that the all of the liquid was the same temperature,

meaning that when they calculated the total amount of heat energy in the whole apparatus at the end of the experiment they greatly over-estimated it. *This is quite tricky. Make sure you can follow the reasoning.*

7 **QWC** *This is a QWC question – see page 76. You need to check your spelling, grammar and punctuation and try to include scientific words, such as 'deuterium' and 'fusion'.*

This question asks you to <u>explain</u> what a control is so make sure you explain why investigations sometimes need a control – don't just describe what a control is.

You should try to include some of the points in the list below. You don't need to make all the points but you should aim to make points with the more stars. If you make 3 or 4 good scientific points in a question like this, and write your answer in good English, you will get 6 marks in an exam. Check your answer with the points below, the grade booster box on page 33 and the general points about QWC answers on page 76.

★ you need a control to see if something is working
★ you could replace one thing that could then act as a control (e.g. water)
★★ a control is usually when the independent variable (input variable) is not applied
★★ a control lets you make comparisons
★★ use normal water (H_2O) as a control, instead of 'heavy water' (D_2O)
★★ or use another metal as a control, instead of palladium
★★★ a control allows you to form a baseline to compare with your other results to see if the changes are only due to the independent variable
★★★ there are two independent variables referred to in Figure B: the amount of D_2O and the volume of palladium. So replacing either of these with closely related substances will act as a suitable control (e.g. H_2O and a different metal).

P2 GALILEO'S IDEA

1 Qualitative. *It only tells us that the objects landed together ... there are no figures.*

2 100 ms. *There are 1000 milliseconds (ms) in 1 second (s). Multiply 1 s by 1000 to get the figure into ms. In this case, 0.1 s × 1000 = 100 ms. You should have also given 'ms' as the unit.*

3 Galileo's experiment has been done many times by many different people, with the same result. So his experiment is reproducible. The more reproducible a finding is, the more likely it is to be correct.

4 a s = d/t so, s = 176/0.6 = 293 cm/s or 2.93 m/s. *To get this correct you need to have written down the distance fallen by the ball at the end (176 cm) and divided this by the time taken. Each image in the photo is 0.1 seconds apart and there are six images below the starting image, so that means that the ball has taken 0.6 seconds to travel that distance. Also be careful of your units. The units that you give your answer in will depend on which units you used for the distance and the time.*

b He did not have a stopwatch/clock/watch with a small enough resolution.

5 a

Distance (cm)	Time squared (s²)
5	0.01
20	0.04
44	0.09
78	0.16
123	0.25
176	0.36

b *A scatter graph is drawn here because you are looking for relationships/correlations between two qualitative and continuous variables.*

You might have included error bars, which are always a nice touch but you won't lose credit for not including them.

Make sure you have:

- *A title*
- *The dependent variable on the y-axis (distance)*
- *The independent variable on the x-axis (time squared)*
- *A good scale for the y-axis so that the plotted points are well spread*
- *A y-axis scale that has even divisions*
- *A y-axis scale that is numbered*
- *A label for the y-axis with units*
- *A good scale for the x-axis so that the plotted points are well spread*
- *A label for the x-axis with units*
- *An x-axis scale that has even divisions*
- *An x-axis scale that is numbered*

- *All points accurately plotted*
- *All points neatly plotted*
- *A line of best fit drawn using a ruler in the right area of the graph*

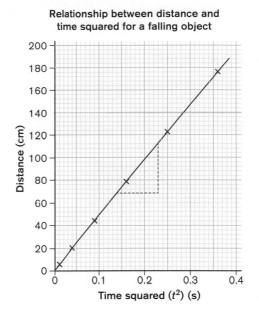

Relationship between distance and time squared for a falling object

c Distance is directly proportional to time squared, or d ∝ t^2. *Try to get into the habit of using symbols.*

d 489 cm/s². The constant of proportionality is calculated from the gradient of the graph.

$$\text{gradient} = \frac{\text{change in } y}{\text{change in } x} = \frac{116 - 72}{0.23 - 0.14} = \frac{44}{0.09} = 489$$

Remember to choose points that are easy to read off your graph when you need to calculate a gradient.

7 You should try to include some of the following points. See also the grade booster box on page 34.

★ flow chart drawn, with the idea coming before the testing

★ statement of Galileo's idea (gravity acts equally on all objects)

★ statement of a prediction (e.g. the objects will hit the ground together)

★ description of experiment

★★ clear statement showing that Galileo's idea about gravity acting equally on all objects is a hypothesis

★★ clear statement showing that Galileo's hypothesis became a theory when experimental results agreed with the prediction

★★ show that other predictions have been made using the theory

★★★ outline other predictions that have been made using Galileo's theory: a hammer and feather will hit the surface of the Moon at the same time when dropped from the same height, a ball and feather will hit the ground at the same time when in a vacuum

P3 PET SCANS

1 a What happens to electrons in different situations?

b **QWC** If this model is correct then positively charged electrons must also exist.

2 a

Cancer number	Volume of cancer (mm³)
1	414
2	606
3	2150
4	697
5	3320
6	3050
7	1950
8	2150
9	1020
10	144

The volume of a sphere needs the equation $4/3 \times \pi \times r^3$. *Don't forget the units in this. The radii were given in mm and so the units will be mm³.*

b Because a cancer is not going to be perfectly spherical.

c *You need to state why scientists use trial runs, for example:*
- it allows you to make sure a method works or
- it allows you to work out what measurements to make in a larger investigation

And then you need to explain your statement, for example:
- so that you don't waste time on taking measurements that do not tell you anything
- so that you don't waste money using equipment that doesn't need to be used

d 5.50 mm – 6.25 mm. The resolution is the smallest radius that can be detected. The smallest of the cancers that could be detected by the PET scanner had a radius of 6.25 mm

and the largest of those that could not be detected had a radius of 5.50 mm. The smallest one that could actually be detected must lie somewhere between these two.

3 **QWC** *There are some examples of answers to this question, and some comments on those answers, on pages 80–81. This is a QWC question – see page 76. You need to check your spelling, grammar and punctuation and try to include scientific words, such as 'radioactive'.*

This question asks you to discuss something, which means that you need to build up an argument about whether it is a good idea or not to use PET scans. You will need to think about the benefits, drawbacks and risks and then put your ideas down in the form of an argument (see S41).

You should try to include some of the points in the list below. You don't need to make all the points but you should aim to make points with the more stars. If you make 3 or 4 good scientific points in a question like this, and write your answer in good English, you will get 6 marks in an exam. Check your answer with the points below, the grade booster box on page 35 and the general points about QWC answers on page 76.

★ identify one benefit of using a PET scanner (e.g. it's good at detecting cancer, it's quick)
★ identify one drawback of using a PET scanner (e.g. expensive, not suitable for small children, not suitable for pregnant women, takes a up a lot of room)
★ identify one risk of using a PET scanner: (e.g. risk of the scan causing cancer in the patient, risk of the scanner causing cancer in the operator)
★★ explain two or more benefits of using a PET scanner (e.g. can detect cancer where other techniques cannot, it's quick and so the patient can get the results quickly and treatment can be started as soon as possible)
★★ explain two or more drawbacks of using a PET scanner (e.g. expensive because the tracers cost a lot to make, not suitable for young children/ pregnant women because the risks of cancer caused by the radioactive tracer are greater)
★★ explain two or more ways in which risks are reduced (e.g. amount of radioactivity used in the tracer is kept to a minimum, the operator is shielded from the equipment)
★★★ PET scans can detect small cancers that cannot be seen using other techniques, for

example in Figure A the eye cancer shows up on the PET scan but not on the CT scan

★★★ only some hospitals have PET scanners, because the tracers need to be made close-by, and so you may have a travel a long way to have a PET scan

★★★ a PET scan increases your risk of getting cancer by 1 in 10 000 and the risk increases for people who are still growing, so children and pregnant women do not usually have PET scans

★★★ an argument written with the same structure as shown in S41

★★★ a clear response given to one counterargument

P4 ON THE SOCKS

1 Controlled variables: the type of socks, the footpath; uncontrolled variables: the sex of the volunteers, the ages of the volunteers, the heights of the volunteers. *There are quite a lot of these and you may be able to think up some more.*

2 a The 'no socks' group since this is the group where the independent variable is not applied.

b Control groups are used when it is difficult to control all the variables. The results from the control group form a baseline to compare with the other results.

3 The reading of 69.4 s in the 'no socks' group is outside the general grouping of the other results

4 a Socks group: slipperiness rating mean = 1.6, time mean = 37.7 s

No-socks group: slipperiness rating mean = 2.9, time mean = 39.6 s

b To come up with an estimate of a measurement's true value.

c You should have drawn one bar chart for the slipperiness and one for the mean time to descend the slope.

You need bar charts here because the independent variable is qualitative but the dependent variable is quantitative, continuous.

You might have included error bars, which are always a nice touch but you won't lose credit for not including them.

Make sure you have:

- *A title*
- *The dependent variable on the y-axis*
- *The independent variable on the x-axis*

- *A good scale for the y-axis so that the plotted points are well spread*
- *A y-axis scale that has even divisions*
- *A y-axis scale that is numbered*
- *A label for the y-axis (with units)*
- *A label for the x-axis*
- *Gaps between the x-axis bars*
- *The categories correctly labelled on the x-axis*
- *All bars accurately plotted*
- *All bars neatly drawn with a ruler (they needn't be coloured)*

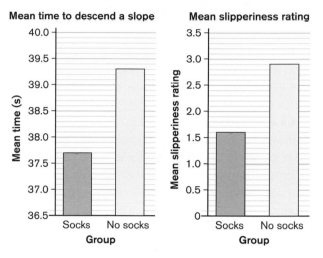

5 People might have fallen and slipped a long way, with a greater likelihood of injury. *It is generally agreed that experiments should not harm people.*

6 So that there is no bias caused by the experimenter because the experimenter does not make the choices. *If the experimenter were allowed to choose which people used the socks and which people didn't, the experimenter might (for example) give the socks to people he/she thought were less likely to slip to prove the idea that socks help. Experimenters sometimes do this even if they don't mean to.*

7 What type of socks are best? Does someone's height determine whether socks outside shoes are helpful? Do socks actually increase the friction between ice and someone's feet? *There are quite a lot of these and you may be able to think up some more.*

8 **QWC** *This is a QWC question – see page 76. You need to check your spelling, grammar and punctuation and try to include scientific words, such as 'risk' and 'hazard'. Note that a 'hazard' and a 'risk' are different things.*

This question asks you to put your ideas down in the form of an argument (see S41).

You should try to include some of the points in the list below. You don't need to make all the points but you should aim to make points with the more stars. If you make 3 or 4 good scientific points in a question like this, and write your answer in good English, you will get 6 marks in an exam. Check your answer with the points below, the grade booster box on page 36 and the general points about QWC answers on page 76.

★ identify something that could cause harm (e.g. ice, flapping bit of sock)

★★ identify one or more hazards (e.g. ice, flappy piece of sock)

★★ identify one or more risks (e.g. risk of slipping on ice, tripping over flappy sock)

★★ identify one or more ways of reducing the risk (e.g. pull the sock properly over the shoe)

★★★ the data from Dr Parkin's investigation shows that people wearing socks over their shoes felt less slipperiness and got down the icy footpath quicker, and so wearing socks over shoes is a good way to reduce the risk of slipping on ice

★★★ include a counterargument (e.g. some people might say that the study was too small to be confident of the results, some people might say that the study concentrated on people's feelings of slipperiness rather than actual quantifiable slipperiness)

★★★ with the slipperiness rating for the 'socks group' being about half that (55%) of the 'no-socks group', this is good evidence that the socks helped to reduce slipperiness

★★★ a clear response given to one counterargument (e.g. some people might say that study concentrated on people's feelings of slipperiness rather than actual quantifiable slipperiness but the people's perception of slipperiness was backed up by the length of time it took them to descend)

★★★ an argument written with the same structure as shown in S41.

P5 SOUND ADVICE

1 12 kHz *Make sure you include the unit.*

2 The measurement for Lucy at 16 000 Hz because it does not follow the trend of the other points.

3 The higher the frequency, the louder the sound has to be to hear it.

4 a micropascals (thousandths of a pascal)

b Using symbols speeds up writing things down, it makes things look clearer (and so you can understand it more quickly), symbols can be understood all over the world no matter what language is spoken. *The best answer will make all three of these points.*

c HIGHER $2 \times 10^6 \mu Pa$ *Don't forget the units.*

d HIGHER $2 \times 10^6 = 2000 \times 10^3$

$2000 \times 10^3 - 5 \times 10^3 = (2000 - 5) \times 10^3 = 1995 \times 10^3$
$= 1.995 \times 10^6 \mu Pa$

The thing to remember is to make all the numbers have the same index. So, you could have done it the other way, and started by converting 5×10^3 (to 0.005×10^6). And don't forget the units!

5 a 17.4 kHz and 60 dB. Both Lucy and Brian will hear the 8 kHz sound at all the loudness settings. At 17.4 kHz, at 40 dB Brian can't hear it but Lucy can only just hear it so it may not be very effective. At 60 dB Brian can't hear it but Lucy can. At 100 dB Brian and Lucy can both hear it.

b Yes. Using two people does not get enough data to draw a conclusion. Secondary data would give the shopkeeper information about the frequencies heard by hundreds/thousands of people in different age groups, without having to do the investigations.

6 This is not a valid conclusion since 25 000 Hz was not tested. *You can't really extrapolate this data because it's not a regular line (e.g. a straight line). It looks as if Brian would not be able to hear sounds in this range but his hearing is not necessarily the same as all adults and this frequency was not tested.*

7 QWC *This is a QWC question – see page 76. You need to check your spelling, grammar and punctuation and try to include scientific words, such as 'frequency'.*

Notice that the question asks you to explain how you would go about doing something; it does not ask you to reach a decision. When answering questions like this, think about financial costs, effects on different groups people, effects on the environment and ethics. Then think about what you already know and what you need to find out in order to reach a decision.

You should try to include some of the points in the list below. You don't need to make all the points but you should aim to make points with the more stars. If you make 3 or 4 good scientific points in a question like this, and write your answer in good English, you will get 6 marks in an exam. Check your answer with the points below, the grade booster box on page 37 and the general points about QWC answers on page 76.

★ identify a benefit of installing the HPDD (e.g. the shop may make more money if people aren't put off by youths outside it, it's more convenient than asking people to move away from the shop the whole time)

★ identify a drawback of installing the HPDD (e.g. costs money)

★ you need to know if the HPDD works

★★ in making a decision you need to balance the benefits and the drawbacks

★★ find out whether it will affect animals in the environment

★★ find out how it will affect people using the shop

★★ find out whether it is fair on people using the shop and passers-by.

★★★ find out the frequencies that animals can hear (e.g. bats) and work out whether the sound might disturb them and so harm the environment

★★★ find out whether the sound will upset babies and cause concern for their parents (who may not be able to hear the noise)

★★★ decide whether installing it will have a good effect for more people than it has a bad effect on, and so be able to justify this as an ethical decision

P6 ASTRONOMICAL

1 a His hypothesis explained why planets appeared to become brighter and dimmer at different times of the year and why some planets appeared to go backwards at some times in the year. *For explanations, see the answer to question 7.*

b The prediction that parallax would be observed for stars was shown to be correct. The hypothesis could now explain all the observations and had a lot of evidence to support it so it became a theory.

2 The resolution of the instruments was not good enough to detect the parallax in the 16th century. *This was a time before even telescopes had been invented.*

3 $1/60 \times 1/60 = 1/3600$

4 a $3.15/1409 = 0.002236$ arcseconds/pixel. Pluto's width is 48 pixels and so, $48 \times 0.002236 = 0.1073$ arcseconds. *The answer is given to 4 significant figures because the pixels at the start are given to 4 significant figures. If you have given your answer to 3 significant figures, this will still be correct.* ⬆ *Although the question didn't ask you to show your working, you won't get any credit for an answer that is wrong and shows no working. And don't forget the units.*

b 1073/10000 *or if you have used fewer significant figures in your answer you may have got 107/1000.*

c $0.1073 \times 1/60 = 0.1073 \times 0.0167 = 0.001791$ arcminutes *or 0.00179 to three significant figures.*

5 a You need to have drawn a scatter graph because you are looking for relationships/correlations between two qualitative and continuous variables.

Make sure you have:
- *A title*
- *The dependent variable on the y-axis (distance)*
- *The independent variable on the x-axis (parallax)*
- *A good scale for the y-axis so that the plotted points are well spread*
- *A y-axis scale that has even divisions*
- *A y-axis scale that is numbered*
- *A label for the y-axis with units*
- *A good scale for the x-axis so that the plotted points are well spread*
- *A label for the x-axis with units*
- *An x-axis scale that has even divisions*
- *An x-axis scale that is numbered*
- *All points accurately plotted*
- *All points neatly plotted*

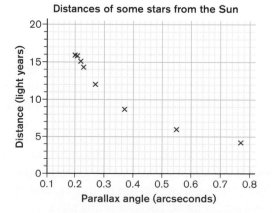

Distances of some stars from the Sun

b **HIGHER** They are inversely proportional. *You can tell this because the graph is a steady curve that slopes down to the right.*

6 a **HIGHER** It would shorten the calculated distances between the Sun and the stars. *For inversely proportional variables, as one variable increases the other decreases and vice versa.*

   b Systematic. This is because all the parallaxes were overestimated.

7 **QWC** *This is a QWC question – see page 76. You need to check your spelling, grammar and punctuation and try to include scientific words, such as 'parallax' and 'theory'.*

   Note that you are asked to explain things in this question. So don't just describe the observations.

   You should try to include some of the points in the list below. You don't need to make all the points but you should aim to make points with the more stars. If you make 3 or 4 good scientific points in a question like this, and write your answer in good English, you will get 6 marks in an exam. Check your answer with the points below, the grade booster box on page 39 and the general points about QWC answers on page 76.

   ★ identify two or more observations (e.g. the planets get brighter and dimmer, stars will show parallax, some planets appear to go backwards at certain times of the year)

   ★ state Copernicus' theory that the Earth went around the Sun

   ★★ if the Earth is further from a planet it will look dimmer, and as the Earth moves it gets closer to a planet making it look brighter

   ★★ if you look at a fixed object from different places, its position seems to change against the background. Since the Earth is moving, you expect to see closer stars moving across the background of more distance stars.

   ★★ the reason why some planets appear to go backwards against the pattern of stars is a parallax effect. *Look at Figure B and imagine that the star is a planet, and the Earth moves down the page to viewpoint B. The 'planet' appears to move up the page against the background of stars as this happens. However, once the Earth starts to move back up towards viewpoint A, the 'planet' will now appear to be going in the other direction.*

   ★★★ if everything were revolving around the Earth, the Earth would not be moving and so there would be no parallax of the stars

   ★★★ if everything were revolving around the Earth, all the planets would be seen to be circling around the Earth and so not go backwards

   ★★★ if everything were revolving around the Earth, the planets would remain at a constant distance and so would not get brighter and dimmer

P7 SPF

1 a By using a sunscreen. *This is the expected answer but you'll get credit for other sensible suggestions like wearing a hat/clothes, not going outside, sitting in the shade.*

   b People are more concerned about hazards that can cause long-term harm than those that cause short-term harm or cancer is perceived to be more dangerous.

2 a The SPF number of the sunscreen.

   b Two from: the amount of sunscreen, the thickness of the sunscreen smear, the brand/type of sunscreen, the amount of UVB radiation reaching each part of the card.

3 150 mins. *The SPF is a ratio, so $15 = x/10$. So, $15 \times 10 = x = 150$. However, note that this is only if you apply enough of the sunscreen (which many people don't) and if you don't go swimming or sweat too much, which makes the sunscreen come off your skin.*

4 The ones of the SPF 30 sunscreen. *These three readings are the most different from one another.*

5 a SPF 4 = 73; SPF 8 = 133; SPF 15 = 276; SPF 30 = 676; SPF 50 = 1915

   b You need to have drawn a scatter graph because you are looking for relationships/correlations between two qualitative and continuous variables.

   You might have included error bars, which are always a nice touch but you won't lose credit for not including them.

   Make sure you have:
   - *A title*
   - *The dependent variable on the y-axis (time for colour change)*
   - *The independent variable on the x-axis (SPF number)*
   - *A good scale for the y-axis so that the plotted points are well spread*

- *A y-axis scale that has even divisions*
- *A y-axis scale that is numbered*
- *A label for the y-axis with units*
- *A good scale for the x-axis so that the plotted points are well spread*
- *A label for the x-axis with units*
- *An x-axis scale that has even divisions*
- *An x-axis scale that is numbered*
- *All points accurately plotted*
- *All points neatly plotted*
- *(A line of best fit drawn using a ruler, if you've done one)*

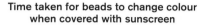

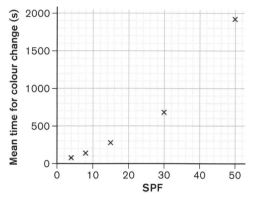

Time taken for beads to change colour when covered with sunscreen

c The greater the SPF number, the longer the bead takes to change colour.

6 *This question could be set as a QWC question, in which case there would be marks for structure, grammar, spelling and punctuation. Only the main points are listed here.*

- The investigation is valid since it is measuring the effect of blocking UVB rays getting to the skin, which would otherwise cause skin damage.
- The measurements are valid and measure how well the sunscreen blocks the UVB rays.
- However, some of the results are not very precise and it would be better to have done more repeat measurements, particularly for the SPF 30 sunscreen.
- The results are accurate enough to draw a conclusion because all of the results, even the less precise set, show a gradual increase in UVB protection as the SPF number increases.
- Apart from one set of the results the measurements were repeatable.
- The results are unbiased but no conclusion has been drawn.

7 **QWC** *This is a QWC question – see page 76. You need to check your spelling, grammar and*

punctuation and try to include scientific words, such as 'ultraviolet', 'rays', 'ozone', 'SPF', 'hypothesis'.

This question asks you to give your opinion and to explain how you came to this opinion from the information given in both P7 and B9.

You should try to include some of the points in the list below. You don't need to make all the points but you should aim to make points with the more stars. If you make 3 or 4 good scientific points in a question like this, and write your answer in good English, you will get 6 marks in an exam. Check your answer with the points below, the grade booster box on page 40 and the general points about QWC answers on page 76.

★ state a reason for sunbathing (e.g. lets the skin make vitamin D, relieves stress)
★ state a reason against sunbathing (e.g. causes sunburn, too much sun can damage the skin permanently, can cause skin cancer)
★ use scientific terms (e.g. ultraviolet rays, ozone, SPF, hypothesis)
★★ use information from both pages, including references to the data and graphs
★★ answer structured in paragraphs
★★ scientific terms used and spelled correctly
★★★ information synthesised (put together) from both pages (e.g. use the risks on page 20 (B9) together with ways of reducing the risk from page 40 (P7); describe the effects of UVA rays from 40 (P7) along with the effects of UVB rays from 20 (B9))
★★★ answer structured in the form of an opinion, which is then backed up with paragraphs each making a central point that is backed up with evidence from the pages. Finishes with a clear concluding paragraph.

P8 SPEED LIMITS

1 a km/h

b Compound units are formed from two or more other units.

2 a Total travel time is (10 mins 4 s) – (3 mins 2 s) = 604 s – 182 s = 422 s. *You can ignore the 14 hours in this case. The 14 refers to 2 pm.*

b 422 s = 422 ÷ 60 mins = 7.03 mins = 7.03 ÷ 60 hours = 0.117 hours. Speed is distance ÷ time, so 7 ÷ 0.117 = 59.8 mph. *Don't forget the units.*

c 10% of 50 = 10/100 × 50 = 5. Cars going above 50 + 5 + 2 = 57 mph will get a fine. Yes, this driver will be fined.

3 HIGHER 15 mins = 0.25 hours. 40 × 0.25 = 10 km. *Don't forget the units! A common mistake here is to forget to convert the minutes into hours. You need to use the same units for time for both the time and the speed. And here, you also need to re-arrange the equation so that it becomes distance = speed × time.*

4 0.279 = 27.9%

5 HIGHER This is the value at which 85% of the data is cut off. In this case it is the speed at or below which 85% of drivers are travelling.

6 You need to draw a histogram here because the independent (input variable) is continuous but has been grouped.

Make sure you have:

- *A title*
- *The dependent variable on the y-axis*
- *The independent variable on the x-axis*
- *A good scale for the y-axis so that the plotted points are well spread*
- *A y-axis scale that has even divisions*
- *A y-axis scale that is numbered*
- *A label for the y-axis*
- *A good scale for the x-axis so that the data is well spread*
- *A label for the x-axis*
- *No gaps between the x-axis bars*
- *An x-axis scale that has even divisions*
- *The categories correctly labelled on the x-axis (you may have labelled the groups as shown or drawn a scale)*
- *All bars accurately plotted*
- *All bars neatly drawn with a ruler*

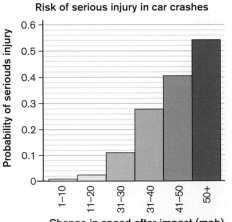

Risk of serious injury in car crashes

Change in speed after impact (mph)

7 QWC *This is a QWC question – see page 76. You need to check your spelling, grammar and punctuation and try to include scientific words.*

There is no right or wrong answer for this question. It is how your use the information and structure your answer that matters.

You should try to include some of the points in the list below. You don't need to make all the points but you should aim to make points with the more stars. If you make 3 or 4 good scientific points in a question like this, and write your answer in good English, you will get 6 marks in an exam. Check your answer with the points below, the grade booster box on page 41 and the general points about QWC answers on page 76.

★ state that you think the article is good or poor with some sort of reason

★ a comment made that the article has good spelling and grammar

★★ use evidence from the page to explain why the article is good or poor

★★ answer structured in paragraphs

★★ scientific terms used and spelled correctly

★★ there is evidence for the claims made (about using the 85th percentile and the increased risk of serious injury). This is a good point about the article.

★★ the evidence is not that up to date (the data in the table is from 1994 and the date of the data in the graph is from the 1950s and 1960s). This is a poor point about the article.

★★ the article presents two arguments about increasing speed limits – one for and one against. This is a good point about the article.

★★ none of the sources of information are revealed. This is a poor point about the article.

★★★ write a concluding paragraph, summarising your reasons for thinking that the article is good or bad

★★★ make suggestions for additional information needed in the article and why it is needed (e.g. data is needed showing how increasing the speed limit has changed the number of accidents, because the risk of serious injury with speed is not really relevant if the actual number of accidents remains the same or falls with higher speed limits)

1 a He measured the sensitivity of the LDR and the photodiode.

b Two from:
- to work out the range of measurements needed
- to work out the interval needed between the measurements
- to work out how many measurements to take
- to work out how many repeat readings to take
- to make sure that you don't make unnecessary readings in the full investigation
- to make sure a method works, and you have the correct apparatus
- to make sure that you have accurate enough measuring apparatus
- to make sure that your investigation is safe.

2 0.2 – 1.0 = 0.8 m *Remember that the independent (input) variable is the variable that the experimenter changes.*

3 a *Your circuit diagram doesn't need to look exactly like this but it must have the three symbols shown (in any order) and must be drawn using a ruler!*

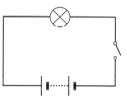

b You need a Venn diagram here because you are trying to show the associations between different groups.

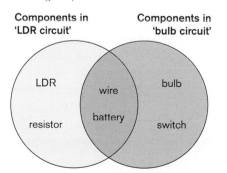

Components in 'LDR circuit'   Components in 'bulb circuit'

LDR

wire

bulb

resistor   battery   switch

4 The sensitivity is how small a change something can detect. The LDR could detect smaller changes in light level than the photodiode.

5 2 V

6 a (0.22 – 0.21) ÷ 0.21 = 0.048 which is 0.048 × 100 = 4.8%

(0.46 – 0.43) ÷ 0.43 = 0.07 which is 0.07 × 100 = 7%

(0.75 – 0.79) ÷ 0.79 = – 0.051 which is – 0.051 × 100 = – 5.1% *This is a negative number because the prediction is lower than the actual value. However, if you have calculated it as a positive number that's also fine. Using the negatives just helps you to answer the next question.*

b Random error. *It's random because with a systematic error all the predictions would be higher or lower than the actual values (not a mixture of higher and lower).*

c Not reading the voltages/distances correctly. Or light sometimes getting to the LDR from other sources (not just the reflection from the board). This investigation would need to be done in a dark room but it's difficult to make the room totally dark the whole time.

7 **QWC** *This is a QWC question – see page 76. You need to check your spelling, grammar and punctuation and try to include scientific words, such as the correct terms for the units.*

This question asks you to evaluate a single thing. So you need to say how good or poor the investigation is based on the list of things to check given in S42.

You should try to include some of the points in the list below. You don't need to make all the points but you should aim to make points with the more stars. If you make 3 or 4 good scientific points in a question like this, and write your answer in good English, you will get 6 marks in an exam. Check your answer with the points below, the grade booster box on page 42 and the general points about QWC answers on page 76.

★ it would have been better if the measurements had been repeated
★ the conclusion matches the hypothesis
★ the measuring devices were accurate enough for this investigation
★★ the investigation is valid: the results allow you to answer the question
★★ the conclusion is valid because it is only drawn from the results
★★ the data for the graph was of good quality because, although there were no repeated measurements, the results obtained for the graph in Figure B all fit neatly on a regular curve.
★★★ the conclusion would be better (more certain) if more measurements had been taken

for the second part of the investigation. A set of only three measurements does not provide very strong evidence that this way of measuring distances is not accurate.

★★★ it would have been better to draw a curve of best fit through the points on the graph because the variables seem to have an inverse relationship

P10 LHC

1 What is dark matter? Or does dark matter exist? And what is dark energy? Or does dark energy exist?

2 You need a pie chart here because you are showing the different proportions that contribute to a whole.

The angles you need are 16° (Particles 4.6%), 83° (Dark matter 23%), 261° (Dark energy 72.4%). *You'll find that when you calculate the angles and round them up to 2 significant figures, that you end up with a total of 361°. So, the easiest solution is to round down the figure with the lowest 'remainder'.*

Make sure you have:

- *The correct angles*
- *A title*
- *All the categories neatly labelled*
- *Used a ruler to draw the lines*
- *Used a compass or similar to draw the circle*

What the Universe is made of

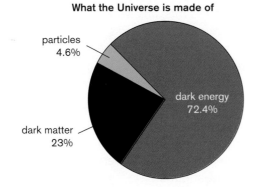

particles 4.6%

dark energy 72.4%

dark matter 23%

3 a *9. There are nine figures in the value.*

b **HIGHER** $2.99792458 \times 10^8 - 3 = 299\,792\,458 - 3$
$= 299\,792\,455 = 2.99792455 \times 10^8$ m/s
or $2.99792458 \times 10^8 - 3 = (2.99\,792\,458 - 0.00000003) \times 10^8 = 2.99792455 \times 10^8$ m/s

Remember that to add or subtract using standard form you need to convert the numbers to the same power of 10.

c **HIGHER** 2.99792455×10^8 m/s
$= 2.99792455 \times 10^5$ km/s
time = distance/speed
$= 27/(2.99792455 \times 10^5)$
$= 9.00623066 \times 10^{-5}$ s

To calculate the speed you need to get the distance in the same units as the distance measurement in the speed unit. And also remember that to divide using standard form you need to divide the big numbers and subtract the indices.

d $(2.99792458 \times 10^8) \times (1 \times 10^9) = 0.3$ m/ns

4 Benefits: allows us to find out more about how the Universe works, will improve things like medical imaging and/or the internet. Drawback: enormous cost

5 a **QWC** The expansion of the Universe depends on 'dark energy'.

b There are two ways: some scientists will review the papers that the LHC scientists write (to make sure that the results and conclusions are valid) and other scientists will then start trying other experiments that could reconfirm the results. *The LHC is not the only 'particle accelerator' in the world, although it is the most powerful, so other scientists might be able to repeat the experiment in other particle accelerators.*

6 *You should try to include some of the following points. See also the grade booster box on page 43.*

★ flow chart drawn
★ clear statement of Zwicky's idea of 'dark matter' included
★ clear prediction (e.g. the mass of the galaxies)
★★ theory of the Universe used to make a prediction about the mass of a galaxy/some stars
★★ prediction is not correct and so a new hypothesis (dark energy) is constructed
★★★ Zwicky's hypothesis added to the other hypotheses that make up the theory of the Universe

Skills Statements

QWC Skills

Skill type	Skill number	Skill statement	Topic	Topic title	Page
QWC	1	legibility of text; accuracy of spelling, punctuation and grammar; clarity of meaning	S48	Analysing and synthesising	72
			S49	Note-taking and formal writing	73
QWC	2	selection of a form and style of writing appropriate to purpose and to complexity of subject matter	S41	Arguments	68
			S43	Exchanging scientific ideas	69
			S47	Science in the media	72
			S48	Analysing and synthesising	72
			S49	Note-taking and formal writing	73
			S50	Command words	74
QWC	3	organisation of information clearly and coherently; use of specialist vocabulary where appropriate	S39	Conclusions	67
			S41	Arguments	68
			S43	Exchanging scientific ideas	69
			S48	Analysing and synthesising	72
			S49	Note-taking and formal writing	73

Maths Skills

Skill type	Skill number	Skill statement	Topic	Topic title	Page
Maths	1	understand number size and scale and the quantitative relationship between units	S6 S9	The SI system Compound measures	47 49
Maths	2	understand when and how to use estimation	S11 S20	Estimates: Rounding and samples Means and ranges	50 54
Maths	3	carry out calculations involving +, −, ×, ÷, either singly or in combination, decimals, fractions, percentages and positive whole numbers	S11 S7 S9 S20 S26 S27 S29	Estimates: Rounding and samples Index form Compound measures Means and ranges Symbols and conventions Fractions, percentages, ratios and decimals Probability	50 48 49 54 58 58 60
Maths	4	provide answers to calculations to an appropriate number of significant figures	S18	Significant figures	54
Maths	5	understand and use the symbols =, <, >, ~	S11 S26	Estimates: rounding and samples Symbols and conventions	50 58
Maths	6	understand and use direct proportion and simple ratios	S27 S35	Fractions, percentages, ratios and decimals Gradients and proportion	58 64
Maths	7	calculate arithmetic means	S20	Means and ranges	54
Maths	8	understand and use common measures and simple compound measures such as speed	S9	Compound measures	49
Maths	9	plot and draw graphs (line graphs, bar charts, pie charts, scatter graphs, histograms), selecting appropriate scales for the axes	S31 S32 S33 S34 S38	Bar charts Histograms Line graphs Scatter graphs Presenting data	61 62 62 63 66

Skill type	Skill number	Skill statement	Topic	Topic title	Page
Maths	10	substitute numerical values into simple formulae and equations using appropriate units	S40	Models	67
Maths	11	translate information between graphical and numeric form	S31 S32 S33 S34 S36 S37 S38	Bar charts Histograms Line graphs Scatter graphs Pie charts Venn diagrams Presenting data	61 62 62 63 65 65 66
Maths	12	extract and interpret information from charts, graphs and tables	S1 S30 S31 S32 S33 S34 S36 S37 S38	The scientific method Tables Bar charts Histograms Line graphs Scatter graphs Pie charts Venn diagrams Presenting data	44 60 61 62 62 63 65 65 66
Maths	13	understand the idea of probability	S29 S45	Probability Risks and decisions	60 70
Maths	14	calculate area, perimeters and volumes of simple shapes	S11 S7 S8	Estimates: rounding and samples Index form Calculating perimeters, areas and volumes	50 48 48
Maths	15*	interpret, order and calculate with numbers written in standard form	S10	Standard form	49
Maths	16*	carry out calculations involving negative powers (only −1 for rate)	S9 S10	Compound measures Standard form	49 49
Maths	17*	change the subject of an equation	S40	Models	67
Maths	18*	understand and use inverse proportion	S35	Gradients and proportion	64
Maths	19*	understand and use percentiles and deciles	S28	Percentiles, deciles and quartiles	59

*These statements are 'Higher Tier only'.

HSW Skills

Skill type	Skill number	Skill statement	Topic	Topic title	Page
Data, evidence, theories and explanations					
HSW	1a	explain what scientific data is	S5	Qualitative and quantitative data	46
HSW	1b	explain how scientific data is collected and analysed	S1 S11	The scientific method Estimates: rounding and samples	44 50
HSW	2a	describe how data is used by scientists to provide evidence that increases our scientific understanding	S1 S4	The scientific method Theories	44 46
HSW	2b	describe the importance of creative thought in the development of hypotheses and theories	S3	Hypotheses and predictions	45
HSW	3a	describe how phenomena are explained using scientific theories and ideas	S1 S4	The scientific method Theories	44 46
HSW	3b	describe how phenomena are explained using scientific models	S40	Models	67
HSW	4a	identify questions that science cannot currently answer, and explain why these questions cannot be answered	S2	Scientific questions	45
HSW	4b	identify questions that science cannot address, and explain why these questions cannot be addressed	S2	Scientific questions	45
Practical and enquiry skills					
HSW	5a	plan to test a scientific idea, answer a scientific question, or solve a scientific problem by choosing appropriate resources	S23 S30	Trial runs Tables	56 60
HSW	5b	plan to test a scientific idea, answer a scientific question, or solve a scientific problem by controlling relevant variables	S13 S14 S30	Variables and fair tests Controls Tables	51 52 60
HSW	5c	plan to test a scientific idea, answer a scientific question, or solve a scientific problem by selecting appropriate data to test a hypothesis	S5	Qualitative and quantitative data	46

Skill type	Skill number	Skill statement	Topic	Topic title	Page
HSW	6	collect data from primary or secondary sources, including the use of ICT sources and tools	S6	The SI system	47
			S8	Calculating perimeters, areas and volumes	48
			S25	Primary and secondary data	57
			S30	Tables	60
HSW	7a	work accurately – individually and with others, when collecting first-hand data	S12	Samples and bias	51
			S16	Accuracy, bias and precision	53
			S17	Errors in measurements	53
			S19	Anomalous results and outliers	54
HSW	7b	work safely – individually and with others, when collecting first-hand data	S24	Safety: risks and hazards	57
HSW	8	evaluate data collection methods and the quality of evidence in terms of validity, repeatability and reproducibility	S17	Errors in measurements	53
			S19	Anomalous results and outliers	54
			S21	Validity	55
			S22	Repeatability and reproducibility	56
			S42	Evaluating	68
Communication skills					
HSW	9	recall, analyse, interpret, apply and question scientific information or ideas	S15	Correlations	52
			S20	Means and ranges	54
			S28	Percentiles, deciles and quartiles	59
			S29	Probability	60
			S35	Gradients and proportion	64
			S39	Conclusions	67
			S40	Models	67
			S41	Arguments	68
			S42	Evaluating	68
HSW	10	use qualitative and quantitative approaches when presenting scientific ideas and arguments	S5	Qualitative and quantitative data	46
			S20	Means and ranges	54
			S28	Percentiles, deciles and quartiles	59
			S29	Probability	60
			S41	Arguments	68

Skill type	Skill number	Skill statement	Topic	Topic title	Page
HSW	11a	present information, develop an argument and draw a conclusion, using scientific, technical and mathematical language, and ICT tools	S6	The SI system	47
			S7	Index form	48
			S8	Calculating perimeters, areas and volumes	48
			S9	Compound measures	49
			S10	Standard form	49
			S30	Tables	60
			S31	Bar charts	61
			S32	Histograms	62
			S33	Line graphs	62
			S34	Scatter graphs	63
			S36	Pie charts	65
			S37	Venn diagrams	65
			S39	Conclusions	67
			S40	Models	67
			S41	Arguments	68
HSW	11b	present information using scientific conventions and symbols	S26	Symbols and conventions	58
			S35	Gradients and proportion	64
			S40	Models	67

Applications and implications of science

Skill type	Skill number	Skill statement	Topic	Topic title	Page
HSW	12	describe the benefits, drawbacks and risks of using new scientific and technological developments	S44	Benefits, drawbacks and risks	70
			S45	Risks and decisions	70
HSW	13a	explain how and why decisions about uses of science and technology are made	S45	Risks and decisions	70
			S46	Decisions about science	71
HSW	13b	explain how and why decisions that raise ethical issues about uses of science and technology are made	S46	Decisions about science	71
HSW	13c	describe the social, economic and environmental effects of decisions about the uses of science and technology	S46	Decisions about science	71
HSW	14	describe how scientists share data and discuss new ideas, and how over time this process helps to reduce uncertainties and revise scientific theories	S43	Exchanging scientific ideas	69
			S47	Science in the media	72
			S48	Analysing and synthesising	72

Glossary

Identifiers	Word	Definition
S16, S42	accuracy	How close a measurement (or set of measurements) is to the real value of something.
S19, S34, S42, S43	anomalous result	A measurement that does not fit the same pattern as other measurements from the same experiment.
S7, S8	area	The amount of surface that a shape has.
S41, S47, S48	argument	Telling people what you believe and why, usually with reasons why you do not agree with others.
S50	assess	Command word in questions that means the same as 'evaluate'.
S42	assumption	Something that everyone accepts as true so you don't test it when doing an investigation, e.g. the Earth is like a ball.
S31, S38	bar chart	Chart showing solid columns, used to present data. It is often used when the independent variable is qualitative.
S44	benefit	Something good that could come from an action or device.
S12, S16, S42, S43	bias	If evidence is shifted in a particular direction it shows bias.
S50	calculate	Command word in questions, meaning work out an answer using numbers. Always show your working. Always put in the units.
S5, S31	categoric data	Data that is not in the form of numbers. Also called qualitative data.
S15	causal correlation	A correlation caused by the independent variable directly affecting the dependent variable.
S8	circumference	The distance around the outside of a circle.
S50	compare	Command word in questions, meaning describe the differences/similarities between things or their advantages/drawbacks.
S50	complete	Command word in questions, meaning fill in answers in a space or finish writing a sentence.
S9	compound measure	A unit of measurement made up of more than one unit (e.g. m/s).
S9	compound unit	Another term for 'compound measure'.
S39, S41, S42, S43	conclusion	A decision made after looking at all the evidence.
S35	constant of proportionality	Symbol is often 'm'. The amount that the values on the x-axis are multiplied by to become the same as the values on the y-axis so that $y = mx$.

Identifiers	Word	Definition
S5, S32, S34	continuous data	Data in which each value can be any number between two limits.
S14	control	In an experiment, a control uses exactly the same set-up as the main part of the experiment but without the independent variable.
S14	control experiment	An experiment in which a control (or control group) is used.
S14	control group	A control for an experiment that consists of a group of things (usually organisms).
S13, S21, S30	control variable	A variable that needs to be controlled in an experiment, otherwise it will affect the results.
S15	correlation	A link between two variables, so that when one changes so does the other one.
S41	counterargument	A reason for not agreeing with an argument.
S34	curve of best fit	A regular curve drawn through a set of points on a graph so that about half the points are above the line and half are below it.
S5	data	Numbers, words, etc. that can be organised to give information.
S28	decile	When data is divided into 10 equal parts: the upper limit of the first 10th of the data is the first decile; the upper limit of the second 10th is the second decile, etc.
S27	decimal	A number shown as a single line of digits.
S50	define	Command word in questions, meaning state briefly what something means
S27	denominator	The number below (or after) the line in a fraction.
S13, S30, S31, S32, S33	dependent variable	A variable that depends on the changes of another variable. This is the variable that you measure in an experiment.
S50	describe	Command word in questions, meaning recall facts in an accurate way or say what a diagram or graph shows (e.g. what trend you can see).
S8	diameter	The distance going through the centre of circle from one side to the other.
S35	directly proportional	Two variables are directly proportional when one increases and the other then increases by the same percentage. This written as A ∝ B.
S5	discrete data	Data in which each value can only be one of a limited choice of numbers.
S50	discuss	Command word in questions, which means build up an argument about an issue.

Identifiers	Word	Definition
S44, S45	drawback	Something undesirable that could come from an action or device.
S31, S34	error bar	A line drawn up and down from an averaged point on a graph to show the range of readings for that point.
S11, S50	estimate (verb)	Command word in questions, meaning make a rough calculation.
S11, S20	estimate (noun)	A rough calculation.
S2, S46	ethics	Actions or ideas that a group of people agree are right or wrong. A country's laws are based on ethics.
S50	evaluate	Command word in questions, meaning that you have to say how good or poor something is based on a series of points (criteria). If you are asked to evaluate more than one thing then you need to compare the things (see 'compare' above) and then state which of the things is best, with reasons why you think that.
S42, S43	evaluation	An assessment of how well something does or has done its job.
S4	evidence	Information used to support an idea or show that it is wrong.
S50	explain	Command word in questions, meaning state the reasons why something happens.
S11, S34, S35	extrapolation	Using a part of some data to estimate values outside this part of the data.
S13, S21	fair test	An experiment in which all the control variables are successfully controlled so that the only factor that affects the dependent variable is the independent variable.
S1, S38	flow chart	Set of boxes with arrows showing how to move through the steps of a process, including any choices that may need to be made.
S27	fraction	A number shown as two parts with a line between them. The digit below (or after) the line is the total number of possible parts. The digit above (or in front of) the line is the actual number of parts.
S32	frequency	The number of occurrences of something in a certain time or in a certain area.
S50	give	Command word in questions, meaning state a fact or example.
S35	gradient	The slope of a straight line. Calculated by picking points, and calculating the difference in the values on the y-axis between these two points, and then difference between the two x-values. The gradient is the difference in y divided by the difference in x.
S24, S45	hazard	Something that can cause harm.

Identifiers	Word	Definition
S32, S38	histogram	A chart showing the frequency of something as a series of bars that group together data on a continuous scale.
S17	human error	Errors in measurements caused by the people making the measurements.
S1, S3, S4, S39, S40	hypothesis	A scientific idea that can be tested.
S50	identify	Command word in questions, meaning look at some data or text and pick out a certain part.
S50	illustrate	Command word in questions, meaning give examples in an explanation or description.
S13, S30, S31, S32, S33	independent variable	A variable that does not depend on changes in other variables. This is the variable that you change in an experiment.
S7	index	A small number written above another number or a unit to show how many times it should be multiplied by itself. Plural = indices.
S7	index form	When an index is shown next to a unit or number, it is said to be in index form (e.g. m^2).
S13	input variable	Another term for independent variable.
S27	integer	A number that does not contain fractions. Another term for 'whole number'.
S35	inversely proportional	Two variables are inversely proportional when one changes and the other changes in the opposite way, so that $A \propto 1/B$.
S43	journal	Scientific magazine in which papers are published.
S50	justify	Command word in questions, meaning evaluate (see 'evaluate' above) something by providing evidence for your choice of which is best.
S4	kinetic theory	Theory based on the idea that all matter is composed of particles that move.
S33, S38	line graph	Graph used to present data in which both the independent and dependent variables are in the form of continuous data. Points are joined together with straight lines.
S34	line of best fit	A straight line drawn through a set of points on a scatter graph so that about half the points are above the line and half are below it.
S50	list	Command word in questions, meaning write down key points in a brief way.
S8	mathematical constant	A number that does not change.

Identifiers	Word	Definition
S20	mean	A way of estimating the true value of a measurement by repeating the measurement, adding the results together and dividing the total by the number of repeats.
S47	media	Something through which information travels is a medium. The plural is media. Newspapers, radio and TV are examples of media.
S28	median	The middle value of an ordered data set.
S40	model	Representing a thing or a process in a way that makes it easier for us to understand. Models usually simplify the real nature of something.
S2, S46	morals	Things that you personally believe are right or wrong.
S50	name	Command word in questions, meaning state a fact or give an example.
S27	numerator	The number above (or in front of) the line in a fraction.
S39, S41, S48	opinion	What you think about something.
S19, S34	outlier	See 'anomalous result'.
S50	outline	Command word in questions, meaning state the main points of an argument or of how something happens.
S13	output variable	Another term for dependent variable.
S43, S48	paper	Scientific report written by scientists to tell others about their research. Papers are published in journals.
S43	peer review	Process in which papers are checked by scientists.
S27	percentage	A fraction in which the denominator is 100. Uses the symbol %.
S28	percentile	A value at which a certain percentage of some data is cut off. So the 24th percentile cuts off the first 24% of the values.
S8	perimeter	The distance around the outside edge of a shape.
S8	pi	The ratio of any circle's circumference to its diameter.
S36, S38	pie chart	Diagram in which the different proportions of something are shown as slices of a circle.
S7	power	See 'index'.
S16, S22, S42	precision	How well grouped together a set of measurements are.
S3, S40	prediction	Saying what you think the results of an experiment will be.
S25	primary data	Data that you collect, e.g. by doing an investigation.
S25	primary evidence	The same as 'primary data'.
S29	probability	The chance of something happening, shown as a fraction, a decimal or a percentage.
S46	public enquiry	Series of meetings that anyone can attend and contribute to, which decides for or against a plan.

Identifiers	Word	Definition
S5, S31	qualitative data	Data that is not in the form of numbers. Also called categoric data.
S5, S31, S33	quantitative data	Data that is in the form of numbers.
S28	quartile	When data is divided into four equal parts: the first quartile of the data is the upper limit of the first quarter part; the second quartile is the upper limit of the second quarter part, etc.
S8	radius	The distance from the middle of a circle to its edge.
S12, S29	random	Something that is done without any regularity or conscious thought and is impossible to predict.
S17	random error	Errors in measurements that have no pattern to them.
S20, S23	range	The difference between the highest and lowest measured values in an experiment (usually ignoring anomalous results).
S8, S27	ratio	A comparison between two numbers, usually shown in the form x:y.
S22	reliable	Results that are repeatable and/or reproducible are said to be reliable.
S22, S42, S43, S46	repeatable	Results that have similar values when repeated by the same experimenter.
S22, S42, S43, S46	reproducible	Results that have similar values when repeated by the different experimenters.
S17, S23	resolution	The smallest change that a measuring device can detect.
S24, S44, S45	risk	The chance of harm occurring from a certain hazard or drawback.
S11, S45	sample	A small part of a collection of data. Scientists might never collect all the data but just collect a sample, which they then use to estimate what the rest of the data is like.
S15, S34, S38	scatter graph	Graph used to find correlations between two variables, which are both in the form of continuous data. Lines or curves of best fit are often drawn through the points.
S15, S34	scatter plot	See 'scatter graph'.
S15, S34	scattergram	See 'scatter graph'.
S1	scientific method	A series of steps that scientists take to show whether a scientific idea is right or wrong.
S25	secondary data	Data that you use but that has been collected by other people.
S25	secondary evidence	The same as 'secondary data'.
S17	sensitivity	See 'resolution'.
S6	SI system	System of units used by most scientists around the world.

Identifiers	Word	Definition
S18, S20	significant figures	The number of digits in a value that actually show the size of that value (all the other digits being zeros).
S10	standard form	A way of writing very small or very large numbers using powers of 10 (the number 10 with an index).
S50	state	Command word in questions, meaning write a fact or an example.
S50	suggest	Command word in questions, meaning use your scientific knowledge to work out what is happening in an unfamiliar situation.
S50	summarise	Command word in questions, meaning state the main points of an argument or of how something happens.
S17	systematic error	Errors in measurements that are all shifted in a certain way.
S30, S38	table	Way of recording data in order in columns and rows.
S4	theory	A hypothesis (or set of hypotheses) that is supported by a lot of evidence.
S23	trial run	A cut-down version of an investigation used to work out what measurements to make in the actual investigation.
S50	use the information	Command phrase in questions, meaning use the data given to answer the question.
S21, S39, S42, S46	valid	When something does what it is meant to do.
S5	value	A number together with something that tells you what the number means (e.g. a unit of measurement).
S13	variable	Something that can change and have different values.
S37, S38	Venn diagram	Diagram composed of circles or ovals that show the associations between different groups.
S7, S8	volume	The amount of space that a 3D shape takes up.
S27	whole number	A number that does not contain fractions.
S50	write down	Command phrase in questions, meaning state a fact or give an example in writing.

Key

atomic number → 1	1 ← relative atomic mass (atomic weight)	
	H ← symbol	
	Hydrogen ← name	

Periodic table (values shown as: atomic number, relative atomic mass, symbol, name)

Group 1	2	3	4	5	6	7	8	9	10	11	12	13	14	15	16	17	18
1 · 1 · **H** · Hydrogen																	2 · 4 · **He** · Helium
3 · 7 · **Li** · Lithium	4 · 9 · **Be** · Beryllium											5 · 11 · **B** · Boron	6 · 12 · **C** · Carbon	7 · 14 · **N** · Nitrogen	8 · 16 · **O** · Oxygen	9 · 19 · **F** · Fluorine	10 · 20 · **Ne** · Neon
11 · 23 · **Na** · Sodium	12 · 24 · **Mg** · Magnesium											13 · 27 · **Al** · Aluminium	14 · 28 · **Si** · Silicon	15 · 31 · **P** · Phosphorus	16 · 32 · **S** · Sulphur	17 · 35.5 · **Cl** · Chlorine	18 · 40 · **Ar** · Argon
19 · 39 · **K** · Potassium	20 · 40 · **Ca** · Calcium	21 · 45 · **Sc** · Scandium	22 · 48 · **Ti** · Titanium	23 · 51 · **V** · Vanadium	24 · 52 · **Cr** · Chromium	25 · 55 · **Mn** · Manganese	26 · 56 · **Fe** · Iron	27 · 59 · **Co** · Cobalt	28 · 59 · **Ni** · Nickel	29 · 64 · **Cu** · Copper	30 · 65 · **Zn** · Zinc	31 · 70 · **Ga** · Gallium	32 · 73 · **Ge** · Germanium	33 · 75 · **As** · Arsenic	34 · 79 · **Se** · Selenium	35 · 80 · **Br** · Bromine	36 · 84 · **Kr** · Krypton
37 · 85.5 · **Rb** · Rubidium	38 · 88 · **Sr** · Strontium	39 · 89 · **Y** · Yttrium	40 · 91 · **Zr** · Zirconium	41 · 93 · **Nb** · Niobium	42 · 96 · **Mo** · Molybdenum	43 · 99 · **Tc** · Technetium	44 · 101 · **Ru** · Ruthenium	45 · 103 · **Rh** · Rhodium	46 · 106 · **Pd** · Palladium	47 · 108 · **Ag** · Silver	48 · 112 · **Cd** · Cadmium	49 · 115 · **In** · Indium	50 · 119 · **Sn** · Tin	51 · 122 · **Sb** · Antimony	52 · 128 · **Te** · Tellurium	53 · 127 · **I** · Iodine	54 · 131 · **Xe** · Xenon
55 · 133 · **Cs** · Caesium	56 · 137 · **Ba** · Barium	57 · 139 · **La** · Lanthanum	72 · 178.5 · **Hf** · Hafnium	73 · 181 · **Ta** · Tantalum	74 · 184 · **W** · Tungsten	75 · 186 · **Re** · Rhenium	76 · 190 · **Os** · Osmium	77 · 192 · **Ir** · Iridium	78 · 195 · **Pt** · Platinum	79 · 197 · **Au** · Gold	80 · 201 · **Hg** · Mercury	81 · 204 · **Tl** · Thallium	82 · 207 · **Pb** · Lead	83 · 209 · **Bi** · Bismuth	84 · 210 · **Po** · Polonium	85 · 210 · **At** · Astatine	86 · 222 · **Rn** · Radon
87 · 223 · **Fr** · Francium	88 · 226 · **Ra** · Radium	89 · 227 · **Ac** · Actinium	104 · 261 · **Rf** · Rutherfordium	105 · 262 · **Db** · Dubnium	106 · 263 · **Sg** · Seaborgium	107 · 262 · **Bh** · Bohrium	108 · 265 · **Hs** · Hassium	109 · 266 · **Mt** · Meitnerium	110 · 269 · **Ds** · Darmstadtium	111 · 272 · **Rg** · Roentgenium	112 · 285 · **Cn** · Copernicium	113 · 286 · **Uut** · Ununtrium	114 · 289 · **Uuq** · Flerovium	115 · 289 · **Uup** · Ununpentium	116 · 293 · **Uuh** · Livermorium	117 · 294 · **Uus** · Ununseptium	118 · 294 · **Uuo** · Ununoctium

Lanthanide series

58 · 140 · **Ce** · Cerium	59 · 141 · **Pr** · Praseodymium	60 · 144 · **Nd** · Neodymium	61 · 145 · **Pm** · Promethium	62 · 150 · **Sm** · Samarium	63 · 152 · **Eu** · Europium	64 · 157 · **Gd** · Gadolinium	65 · 159 · **Tb** · Terbium	66 · 162 · **Dy** · Dysprosium	67 · 165 · **Ho** · Holmium	68 · 167 · **Er** · Erbium	69 · 169 · **Tm** · Thulium	70 · 173 · **Yb** · Ytterbium	71 · 175 · **Lu** · Lutetium

Actinide series

90 · 232 · **Th** · Thorium	91 · 231 · **Pa** · Protactinium	92 · 238 · **U** · Uranium	93 · 237 · **Np** · Neptunium	94 · 244 · **Pu** · Plutonium	95 · 243 · **Am** · Americium	96 · 247 · **Cm** · Curium	97 · 247 · **Bk** · Berkelium	98 · 251 · **Cf** · Californium	99 · 252 · **Es** · Einsteinium	100 · 257 · **Fm** · Fermium	101 · 258 · **Md** · Mendelevium	102 · 259 · **No** · Nobelium	103 · 262 · **Lr** · Lawrencium

Index